An Oxfordshire Land Girl

in World War Two

*A Land Girl's story of life on a farm adjacent to
an RAF airfield in WW2. An airfield which,
towards the end of 1940, became the home of
the RAF's Photographic Reconnaissance Unit.*

Published 2004 by PEF Books, Stanford in the Vale

ISBN 0-9549010-0-2

Joan Fahy

Printed and bound by Parchment (Oxford) Ltd
Printworks, Crescent Road, Cowley,
Oxford OX4 2PB

An Oxfordshire Land Girl

Acknowledgements

Firstly to my husband Peter, whose encouragement and interest sustained me during long spells at my word processor. Also to our daughter, Linda whose expertise in editing and re-typing the manuscript is much appreciated.

Also to many good friends who wanted to know 'what Land girls actually did!'

Land girl Ch 1

In that warm September of 1939, nineteen year-old Jane returned to her home in Oxfordshire to join one of the Women's Services, but her abiding memories of those days were of that severe winter. The freezing temperatures, the ice and the deep snow, and the blackout combined to make those first winter mornings and evenings of the war unforgettable. It was in mid-September, after Prime Minister Chamberlain's declaration that England was 'now at war with Germany,' that Jane returned to her parents' home in order to do some kind of war-work. She left a pleasant job in Somerset, where her work had included breaking in young horses for riding, and now decided to join the Women's Land-Army (WLA); Jane was one of the first girls in Oxfordshire to enrol. Early in November she was assigned to a farm near Ewelme. This was fortunate, since she could still live at home, the farm being only two miles away, on the eastern boundary of the newly completed aerodrome at Benson. So began her daily cycle-ride to work in all weathers.

It was a mixed farm of some 800 acres, whose owners, Mr & Mrs Freeman, had previously farmed in Rhodesia. Here, they had a large herd of pedigree Ayrshire cows, with heifers and calves, two fierce- looking bulls, 3,000 hens, three cart-horses, two hunters and four dogs. There had been a large flock of sheep and several pigs, but just before her arrival they had been sold off so that the Freemans could concentrate more on the dairy herd.

During her interview, Jane was instructed by the farmer that her main jobs would be to look after the hens and the newly-born calves; she would also have to wash and grade the hundreds of

1

eggs each day, look after the dogs, and exercise the two hunters. As if this was not enough, she would furthermore have to assist with cleaning-out the milking parlour, the calf-pens, the stables, and help with any field work such as hay-making, harvesting, hoeing, and threshing when the time came around. Jane was keen, although she guessed it would be hard work. She was happy about it on the whole; however, on her very first morning, she quickly became dismayed at the resentment that two of the men on the farm showed towards her. It seemed that they were constantly under the threat of being called-up to join one or other of the fighting forces; in part, this was because farm jobs were being taken over by land girls.

On her second morning, Jane awoke at 5.30am in a freezing cold bedroom that heralded another bitterly cold day. After a cup of tea and a slice of toast, now with margarine only, Jane began to pile on jerseys and her WLA great-coat, ready to cycle to the farm. It was still dark. Opening the door of her parents' house, she felt for her bicycle and switched-on the lamp which, because of the wartime blackout, allowed only a narrow slit of light by which to see. Struck by the bitterly cold air, Jane dashed back inside to get her thick scarf as well as her woolly hat; yet, even with two pairs of gloves on her fingers she felt the chill as soon as she touched the cycle's handlebars. The road to the farm was icy, and very soon her face and feet were frozen. Cycling was hazardous; her eyebrows turned white with frost, which soon coated the fringe of her hair. Trying to pedal fast was not easy but at least warmed her a little, and eventually she reached the farm. After putting her cycle in the barn, she let the dogs out of their kennels and began the long walk up the lane – almost a mile - to the top of the hill, where the chickens were housed. The dogs were a little hesitant to follow at first - they had only

2

met this girl the day before - but as she called their names and fondled their heads they were happy to go along; the frosty morning did not worry them in the least. The oldest farmhand, Benny, knew that she had only been up to the   hill once before, when the farmer was showing her round; so he caught up with Jane and told her he would walk with her since it was still dark. Later, after sunrise, he was going to do some hedging along the field where the hens were housed. She was grateful for his company.

When they finally reached the hen houses, after much slipping and sliding along the icy road, Benny led her across to an old shepherd's hut, telling her that all the foodstuff, hay, straw and other necessities were housed there. Before the door could be opened, its lock had to be thawed; this he did by holding the lock in the warmth of his hands until the ice on it melted. Benny, with his little old pipe still in his mouth, then went in and lit the hurricane lamp so that Jane could find her way to unlock the twenty chicken-houses. Next he showed her how to hold the locks in her gloved hands to thaw them out; while she did this, he lit the stove in the hut, so that she could warm her gloves as they became wet and frozen from the process of defreezing the locks.

Her fingers were numb with cold, her feet frozen, and altogether she felt totally wretched and began to wonder if she would be up to this job. As she opened each door the hungry hens rushed out, eager for their food; Benny called-out to Jane to throw some of the corn on the ground in front of them, 'Else you'm never goin' to be able to move for bodies.' She could see exactly what he meant. 'Next us'll 'eat some water to make their mash, corn ain't enough in weather like this.' Jane soon realised that 3,000

3

hens clucking around her feet, whilst she was trying to get into the huts, were a real hazard!

Benny had looked after them prior to Jane's coming, but with his nose dripping, his old pipe in his mouth, his moustache white with the frost, he was a willing teacher. As time went by on the farm, Jane was to realise that in him she had a real friend, even though they were so far apart in age.

This first morning was difficult, not just because everything was frozen, but because Jane had to find out exactly how much food so many hens needed, learn how to clean out their nesting boxes, break the thick ice to get to the water they required for producing even the limited amount of eggs there would be in these conditions. She discovered yet again that absolutely everything she touched, apart from the actual bodies, froze her fingers to the bone.

Finally the jobs there were completed, and Jane whistled for the dogs and set off back down the long hill. She saw that Benny, with his nose still dripping, was busy slashing, or as some called it, plashing, the overgrown hedge. He called out to her saying, 'I'll keep an eye out for 'ee case any 'ungry foxes are about'. Once more she thanked him for all his help.

When she finally got back to the farmyard, Jane popped her head into the warm milking parlour to ask if she should feed the horses next or start on the calves. She was told that as she'd been so long with the chickens, the second cowman, Paul, had already started on the youngest calves, and so it was to the stables and two hunters that Jane went next. Dobbin, the carter, always looked after the three carthorses himself. Slightly resentful of her, he had already taken a bale of hay across to the hunters, but their cleaning-out he left to Jane. She shyly thanked him and almost got a smile, in fact it was just a grunt, but at least it was a start! One of the hunters belonged to the farmer himself and the other to his wife, so Jane went into the house to ask them what exactly she needed to do. She found them in the kitchen having just finished their breakfast. Mrs Freeman immediately made a hot drink saying, 'You must be frozen starting farm-work on a morning like this!' Jane thanked her, and noticed for the first time that one of her legs was in irons. Seeing her concern, the farmer told Jane that his wife had been crippled following a riding accident several years ago, but that she still loved to do a little gentle hacking. He asked her to sit down and get acquainted with them, which she was glad to do. He outlined once more what her jobs were, adding that if she would exercise his wife's mare when the weather was more suitable, that would be most helpful. Jane was pleased to have her duties spelled out more clearly, and when Mr Freeman left them his wife explained that he was a Naval Reservist and could be called up at any time if required for war service.

Jane eventually left the cosy kitchen to tackle the cleaning-out of the stables. The two horses whinnied as she went in and she guessed that the farmer had fed them as their hay-nets were full and there was water in their buckets. Although it was a bit warmer in there, she still kept on her woolly hat and gloves but was able to discard her coat as the mucking-out exercise warmed her up.

When she'd completed this task it was well after sunrise; her boss came in to tell her that this morning the threshing of one of the cornricks was about to start which meant all 'hands to the pump'. She got her bicycle out and followed him up to the field, where, for the first time in her life she confronted a threshing machine that was about to go into action. This formidable-looking beast was quite close to a rick where two men were taking off the thatch which had been put on previously in order to keep out the wind and rain after the end of harvest. The men there, two of the cowmen, Frank the tractor driver, and the two carters Dobbin and Jack, were all busy preparing for the huge gleaming black engine to start up and the job to begin. The machine's owner was busy using a spirit-level to make sure that the thresher, which was close up to the rick, was completely level. Another man was knocking wooden wedges under the wheels and when all was completed the engine driver stoked-up the fire to raise steam until the belt of the drum-pulley clapped, and grew taut as the drum revolved.

Jane was told to go up the ladder to the top of the rick along with Dobbin and Frank; there they used pitch-forks to dislodge the sheaves so that they fell down onto the platform of the drum. At first, as it warmed her up, she thought this would be easy, but to her dismay she found that she could hardly move a single sheaf. She heard Dobbin mutter, 'I knew ruddy girls would be useless.' But Frank stopped what he was doing and said quietly to her, 'always take the top sheaf, Polly, you'll find it easier'. From then on she managed better. The name 'Polly' was to stick for the whole of her time there.

After what seemed hours to Jane, who had never before seen threshing done let alone taken any part in it, the belt slackened, the men all ceased work and she assumed it was lunchtime. But no, it was only 10:30 and simply a break for a five-minute rest, while they all partook of whatever liquid was in their thermos flasks! Jane, knowing nothing of this, just stood and watched. She was thirsty herself until Frank handed her his flask, telling her to always bring some sort of drink with her in future. She next noticed that the whole area was littered with chaff from the corn and that dust covered each one of them from head to foot; the wheat was already being bagged-up into Hessian sacks, and there seemed to be piles of straw everywhere. No-one was cold though, and the winter sun was attempting to break through.

Suddenly the engine hissed and they all began work again. At least it wasn't quite such a high climb as the rick had by now considerably reduced in height. Jane realized, as she began her task once more that her hands, despite gloves, were extremely sore and her back was beginning to ache as well. It seemed an eternity before everything stopped once more and this time it really was for lunch. She wearily got on to her cycle calling out 'cheerio' to the men, and she noticed that all but the cowman and herself had settled on the ground with their backs to the rick; they had their hunks of bread and cheese and bottles of cold tea. One of them called, 'see you later,' to Jane as she cycled off, but she had other ideas and thought 'not if I can help it!'

Lunch in the farmhouse was hot soup with bread and cheese, followed by a cup of tea, after which Jane almost fell asleep - it was so warm and she was so tired. Mr Freeman roused her saying he thought the morning on the threshing job had been enough for her first day and that she should go over and introduce herself to the young stock, the calves and others. Jane leaped up, as she was eager to meet her young charges, and soon forgot sore fingers and backache.

The calves were simply adorable and all nuzzled-up to her as she entered their pens; even the young four-month-old bull approached her as if wanting a cuddle. The cowman, Arthur, told Jane that the bull was to be one of her charges and that he was leaving it to her to give him a suitable name. He followed this by showing her how and what to feed them and instructed her on their cleaning-out. Arthur had been keen to have Land girls - he felt they had a better way with calves and young stock than did men, and he also knew that Paul, his under-cowman, was looking elsewhere for another farm job, and that finding someone else to do his work here would not be easy.

So life as a Land girl had begun, and Jane fell into a daily routine getting used to the cold, dark, early mornings and the dusky evenings when she was waiting for all her hens to go into their houses to be shut-up for the night. She'd been told that any left out and hiding underneath a house would be a fox's meal by morning. Jane quickly learned about her flock, which were Rhode-Island-Reds. She loved the way they rushed to meet her in the afternoons when she arrived to feed them and collect their eggs. They had peculiar habits, crouching to allow her to rub her fingers on their back feathers, and clucking loud greetings at her every visit. Walking back down, even with only half a basketful of eggs, was quite precarious with one large basket on either side of the cycle handlebars, and potentially disastrous if she slipped on an icy patch.

The newly-born calves had to be taught to drink from a bucket and once she'd learned how, she became accustomed to having very sore fingers as their tiny tongues were extremely rough with a texture like sandpaper. Sometimes she had the heartbreaking task of finding one dead and having to remove its body for investigation, which was carried out by Arthur. Fortunately this

8

did not happen often. Other tasks during the winter days were mucking-out in the milking shed and in the pens of all the young stock. Her muscles became stronger as she pushed loads of heavy manure across the field to the allotted muck heap, which would later be spread in the fields.

Cutting kale when it was frozen was yet another miserable but necessary task, as well as collecting mangolds ready for the chopping machine, and crushing the oats in yet another machine, especially adapted for that purpose; all these jobs were essential for feeding the cattle. There was hay to be cut out from a hay-rick but although she could collect it with a wagon and carthorse, no way would the men allow her to use the extremely sharp cutting tool.

Land girl Ch 2

Winter did eventually pass. The sun began to rise earlier, and the cows could be put out to pasture during the day. Freezing hands became a chilly memory as other seasonal tasks filled Jane's working day; also there were now more eggs to collect, wash and grade.

Although she knew a good deal about horses, the grey mare Daisy and the young chestnut Prince were quite a challenge for her to harness. Being carthorses, they were many hands higher than anything she had tackled before and she had quite a struggle trying to get their collars over their heads, let alone the rest of their harness.

The next sign of the continued resentment at having a 'girl' on the farm came one morning when Dobbin asked her to fetch Prince, already harnessed, and back him into the shafts of a huge water-barrel, then take him to the brook at the end of the farm lane. Using a bucket, she was to fill the barrel with water, and take it to the meadow where the cows would be grazing later.

Filling the barrel from the fast-flowing brook, bucket by bucket, meant a long and tedious task for Jane, leaving her not only pretty wet, but with an aching back before the huge barrel was full. Once she reached the field she backed Prince and the water-barrel up against the trough then, as instructed, pulled the ring of the bung, which allowed the water to flow out. This water-barrel had huge iron wheels, but unfortunately Dobbin had *not* explained to Jane that she mustn't on any account stand near the wheel as she let the water out, *nor* had he told her that Prince was terrified at the sound of rushing water!

Jane stood by the wheel in order to reach the bung but as soon as the water rushed out into the trough Prince took off hell-for-leather, across the field, with the wheel going right over Jane and knocking her senseless. Fortunately, Frank, who was ploughing in the nearby field, saw the horse tearing round and spotting something on the ground, rushed across to find Jane lying unconscious in a wet heap on the ground. Covering her with his jacket he quickly ran back to the farm to get help.

Although very bruised and soaking wet, she soon recovered, but not before both the farmer and Mrs Freeman had checked to make sure no other damage had been done to her; they telephoned her parents to get a doctor in case they'd missed anything. They drove her home where she was checked over by her doctor, who confirmed that no bones were broken, and that she was still suffering from shock. Nevertheless, her parents were not best pleased about the incident nor the reason why it had happened, but then neither were the Freemans. Dobbin was severely reprimanded and was given all Jane's work as well as his own for the next week.

As the weather improved there was a great deal of activity on the aerodrome, which was only a mile from the farm. It was, in fact, right opposite the well-known water-cress beds in the adjacent village of Ewelme, and Jane recalled that, in her younger days, people would flock there to buy the luscious green cress with its sweet aniseed flavour. A huge bunch cut fresh would cost only sixpence, but sadly, as more and more workers were called-up for National Service, the beds had got neglected.

The farmer allowed Jane to sell fresh farm eggs to the airmen, especially at weekends when they might be going home on leave. At these times there would be long queues from the farm to the end of the lane. This extra chore made Jane a very popular person. As the news travelled and, as spring advanced, the hens were laying eggs in great abundance - so much so, in fact, that it was becoming almost impossible for her to manage the two large egg-baskets, almost full to the brim, perilously fixed on either side of the handlebar of her bicycle. Even though she walked carefully, there was inevitably the occasional accident which resulted in smashed eggs spread all over the road; with eggs rationed at one per person each week this was a major disaster.

One morning, after she'd finished all her jobs, Mrs Freeman asked Jane into the farm kitchen for a chat. The girl was somewhat apprehensive wondering what she had done or not done. But the dear lady only wanted to tell her that she and her husband had decided to purchase a pony and a tub-cart so that Jane could bring down the heavy egg-baskets in safety. She also said the pony and cart would be useful for herself - particularly since petrol rationing was beginning to bite much more; she would be able to drive into the village to do her shopping. Jane admitted that she had never seen a 'tub' cart and her lady-boss explained that it was a fairly small, roundish four-sided cart with two large but quite light wheels, a small door at the back, simple wooden bench seats on each side; and shafts that made it easy to pull. Mrs Freeman said that both the pony and cart would be arriving the following morning, and that she and her husband were quite confident that Jane would have no trouble in handling either pony or trap.

Excitement mounted next morning as a lorry arrived with the cart, followed by Mr Freeman with a horse-box, drawn behind his car. Jane went cautiously forward as a fine-looking jet black pony was led out and handed straight to her. She is yours to name as you wish her boss told her, and right away Jane said, 'She has to be 'Blackie' don't you think?' And he agreed. Much to her amazement, Dobbin and Benny appeared and called, 'good on you Polly!' She was further surprised to see that an old disused stable had been made ready by the two farmhands. Blackie was sweating a little from the drive, and was probably a little nervous due to strange voices and handlers, so Jane introduced her to the stable cautiously. After giving her a handful of hay, she rubbed her coat down before leading her along the lane a short way, then finally she showed her the tub-cart. As the stable floor had already been covered with straw Jane took off the pony's halter, closed the bottom half of the door, and left her while she got a bucket of fresh water. To her great delight Blackie gave a gentle whinny and began to drink straight away, stopping only to shake her mane, as if to say 'I needed that!'

The rest of the morning flew by as Jane completed all her usual jobs, and at lunchtime she went into the house hoping to see her boss and his wife, but only Mrs Freeman was there. Jane thanked her for her thoughtfulness in getting the pony and cart, with a wry smile her lady boss reminded her that this would be one extra chore added to those she already had. But Jane replied, 'How very much quicker driving, instead of cycling, to and from the chickens will be, and hopefully no more weary pedalling all that way on my bike.'

Mrs F., as she was now known, asked her if, on her day off, she would ride Blackie to give her a change from pulling the tub, and the delighted girl gladly agreed to this, saying that she would also ride her to shut the hens up as the evenings got lighter and the birds remained outside later.

Apart from her work at the farm Jane had fun times in her own village after her days work. Because there were many RAF and other servicemen and women needing somewhere they could go to relax, the village ladies, members of the Women's Voluntary Service [WVS] provided meals in a local hall where table-tennis, darts and other games could be enjoyed. Jane would often 'look in' and join in with whoever needed a partner; she was an excellent table-tennis player, and not bad at darts either. Her own special friend, Michael, whom she had known since school-days, was away in the north of England training as a bomber pilot. During the last winter many boys she'd known from the village had been posted missing or killed, some in the navy, but most from the army. Michael was the only local boy she knew in the RAF. Other good times were had at the Benson village-hall dances, or 'hops' as they had come to be called. There she was known by all who had purchased precious eggs from the farm, and because of this she was never without dancing partners.

Jane also had another friend who was in the land-army on a farm a few miles from her own. Deborah was blonde in contrast to dark-haired Jane; she was also a far better dancer and much more flirtatious, but unfortunately not particularly happy in her farm work. Sometimes they would go together to the cinema in Wallingford, which was the nearest town, but it was a case of cycling in all kinds of weather and always in the blackout on their return home.

The war news became more and more depressing and the girls naturally grabbed whatever happiness they could in their off-duty times. Occasionally, one of the sergeants would invite Jane to a dance in his mess and on such occasions she always took Deborah along. They were good times mostly, unless one of the pilots had just been reported missing or even known to have been killed, then the evening was sombre, and sometimes not very sober. The girls did their utmost to jolly things up, mostly by telling of various odd things that had happened to them recently on their respective farms; all the same it was, at times, quite an effort for them to keep their spirits up.

As spring gave way to summer, Jane had even more to do with new-born calves arriving daily and many barrels of water to be carted to wherever the cows were grazing; worst of all, the chickens simply would not go into their houses before darkness fell. Consequently, her work-days got longer and longer. Occasionally a friend, or a new RAF acquaintance, would offer to cycle up the hill with her to the chicken houses.

One evening, to her great surprise, her friend Michael appeared, having walked all the way from his home in the village of Benson. He had apparently been to Jane's parents and they had suggested she was probably still waiting for all her hens to go to bed, and as he only had a few days leave he wanted to see her. It was quite some time before they saw the last of the stragglers hop in the 'pigeon-hole' entrance of their house and only then were they able to begin the long walk back.

Michael was tall and handsome with blonde hair and great blue eyes; he and Jane had known one another on and off for most of their lives. They used to cycle to their school in Wallingford together. He was always a quiet person, and this particular evening was even more so until Jane asked him directly what

15

was wrong. Was it anything to do with his pilot-training course? Answering with one of his lovely smiles he told her quietly, 'I'm enjoying the flying but as many of my mates are posted and then we hear that they are 'killed in action,' I can't help wondering how soon it will be my turn.' It was then Jane noticed how very sad his eyes had become as he told her how worried he was about his mother should the inevitable happen. She felt nothing but sympathy for him, for she knew that his mum would be totally alone should such a thing occur, for his father had died quite suddenly several years before.

Michael had volunteered for service in the RAF, as had thousands of other young men of his age, and although both he and his mother had known what a risky job he would be undertaking once he was fully trained for operational duties, his mother had encouraged him to follow his dream. Now, as he told Jane, the time had come; he had a 48-hour pass and then he would be flying with his crew, in a Wellington bomber, on operations over Germany. The tears were not far away as Jane struggled with her own feelings as she listened, knowing how little comfort she could offer him at a time like this. He seemed so very young to be taking on such responsibility, and yet this was war, and the Germans had to be stopped, and the consequences had to be faced.

They spent the rest of the evening in the local pub, the Castle, where they met other friends, also many air-crew and WAAFS, and for a short while even the war could be forgotten. Michael asked Jane if she thought her boss would give her some time off; if so, he wanted to know if she would accompany him to London to see him off. He said 'My leave is up the day after tomorrow. Is that too short notice, but if its okay, will you come?' Jane rang the Freemans as soon as she got home and they said of course she must go once she'd fed and let out the chickens; they would arrange for the calves and her other duties to be taken care of.

It was the first time Jane had been to London since the war had started and she was amazed to see all the bed-rolls, blankets and personal belongings on the underground platforms. She was aware that since the bombing had begun, people did take shelter there, but had no idea that it would be quite like this. The next thing was to telephone the nearest Land-Army hostel to arrange a bed for the night. After a pleasant evening spent together, Jane was more than a little scared being in a hostel room on her own. Fortunately, only one siren went off and the 'all clear' followed soon afterwards; however, it still unnerved her and she had very little sleep. She and Michael met again the following morning and had a wartime breakfast in a Lyons Corner House before going to the station for his train. As it pulled in there were many other couples saying their goodbyes, lots of hugs together with tears, and Jane had a horrible feeling that this might well be *the* goodbye to her friend. She tried hard not to let him see how she felt and promised to write regularly and to see him on his next leave. Michael gave her a quick hug and after thanking her for being there with him, jumped on to the train, not looking back once.

As Jane caught her train back to Oxford she was quite pleased that it was filled with young people who were all in one or other of the forces, and as a young soldier offered her his seat it suddenly came to her how very fortunate she was working on a farm, with animals she loved, in fresh air and not directly connected with the horrors of this war.

Jane knew that she loved Michael, but it was more like sisterly love than anything more romantic; he had always been there for her. But now she had to face the fact that she might never see him again and she found it difficult to fight back her tears.

Land girl Ch 3

Back at work again, Jane enjoyed her early morning rides on Blackie, with the dogs following; the hens soon got used to the pony tethered to the shepherd's hut while they were let out and fed their corn mixture. No need for warm mash, no frozen locks to contend with, but Jane had to make sure that they had water, and the calcareous grit which they needed for their eggs to have good brittle shells. There was also still the once a week job of cleaning-out nesting-boxes and the slats on which the hens perched inside their houses.

On this late Spring morning Jane could hear a great deal of activity coming from the nearby aerodrome and as she looked up she could see Wellington bombers taking off, one after the other. These, with Whitleys and Blenheims were just about all that England had for venturing into enemy territory during the early part of the war. Blackie shivered a little wondering whatever the noise was all about, but soon settled once he heard Jane's soothing voice; she too felt apprehensive, and wondered just how many of them would return. Then, by the end of May, British troops were being evacuated from the beaches of Dunkirk and the fear of a German invasion of Britain was uppermost in the minds of many people.

In the farmyard later that day, Arthur, the cowman asked Jane to take the young bull out for exercise. For some reason, it was that very morning she decided to call him 'Montgomery,' as he pulled and frolicked about, so pleased was he to be out of his pen! Jane had become very fond of the animal, he was a truly fine young pedigree Ayrshire bull. All the same, she soon discovered he took quite some holding, and it seemed that *he* took Jane out rather than vice-versa. Arthur had been watching from a distance and was pleased with the way she'd handled the bull; so, when she was helping to clean out the milking-parlour, he asked if she would like to take 'Monty' to a local show later in the year, should it still be held. The thought of this accolade thrilled her no-end, and it made her feel accepted by the men at long last.

But as more and more cities in the country were being bombed heavily, night after night - most especially London - Jane did wonder if such things as agricultural shows would ever take place again. Just before hay-making began early in June, her boss told Jane that another Land girl would soon be joining them as dairy-maid. This was great news for her, as she had envied the girls who worked in gangs, and had often felt isolated on this farm, a solitary Land girl amongst so many men.

Frank had cut two fields of the long grass which were intended for hay and told her that if the weather remained warm and sunny, they would be turning it in a few days. Meantime, Benny and Jane set about cleaning and disinfecting all the hen-houses inside, prior to creosoting them on the outside. She learned from him that this job had to be done every year in order to prevent disease, because with so many hens using each house throughout the winter months, sickness could easily spread. So far there had been no shortage of corn for feeding them, but as Mrs Freeman had told Jane, there might have to be a major culling-out before the next winter if the war continued.

Hay-making was in full swing next day, and as soon as Jane had seen to the hens and calves she put Blackie's saddle on, leaving the halter on as well as the bridle, and rode her along to the hayfield. The men had been told to 'take it easy' with Jane, and after she'd tied the pony's halter to the nearest tree, she went over to see what her job was to be. Both cart-horses were harnessed into hay-carts, and Dobbin asked her to take the one with Prince across to where Benny had started to build a rick. Her job was to climb on to the load of hay, and using a pitch-fork, throw the hay down to him. Fortunately the rick was quite low at this stage and Jane found it an easy and sweet-smelling task, with Prince behaving perfectly for her this time.

As Jane passed Dobbin who was bringing the next load, she heard Benny shout, 'Us'll need Frank over 'ere after this 'un, it be gettin 'igh enough to 'ave the elevator across.' The 'elevator' was a machine which carried either hay or straw to the highest part of a rick. This was to be yet another new experience for the Land girl, having never used one of these before; she now had to throw the next load of hay on to the elevator as the rick got ever higher.

That afternoon she helped Arthur with the milking. Previously, she had only done this when he or Paul had their weekend off, but today it was 'all hands on deck' in order to get the hay on the rick before the next morning's dew could dampen it. Again it was a long day, and she had promised one of the sergeants to go to his mess dance that evening. Fortunately, seeing how tired she seemed, Arthur offered to shut up the hens for her, adding that the 'missus' had said her own mare wasn't getting nearly enough exercise, all the lovely new grass was making her too fat to ride comfortably, and a good gallop with *his* weight on her back would do her good.

After a quick bath, and wearing a pretty summer-dress, Jane felt more able to face dancing, and when her friend Deborah arrived, her father drove them as far as the guard-room where their escorts were awaiting them. It turned out to be quite an evening; Jane was soon able to forget her sore hands and tiredness and began to enjoy herself. The sergeant who had invited her hit it off rather well with Deborah, which didn't matter, because he had already introduced Jane to Tom, a fellow pilot. Altogether the evening flew, and soon the two young men escorted the girls back - Jane to her home and Deborah to the farm where she worked.

A week later the new Land girl, Pat, arrived. She turned-out to be quite well-built with fair hair and a good sense of humour. She had already arranged to live in at the farm, for her home was in the north of England. Her arrival coincided with the farmer himself being called-up to join the Navy. He was to serve on a Corvette, which was, as his wife told the girls, 'a ship that escorted the convoys across the Atlantic'; they guessed it was yet another dangerous wartime assignment.

The fact that her boss had been called up did not altogether dismay Jane, even though she felt very sorry for his wife, and wondered about the farm's future - as they all did. But recently, Mr Freeman had become somewhat of an embarrassment to Jane; he would be there in the barn where she housed her bicycle every morning and attempt to give her 'a goodmorning' embrace; he would also appear on the hill at the shepherd's hut, on the days when he'd been to the local markets drinking with his farmer friends, and again make advances to her. Jane found this embarrassing and horribly disloyal to his wife. Her friend Deborah had found the same problem with her farmer-boss. It seemed almost that they thought the land-girls were there partly for their pleasure. Here, Jane found a great pal in Frank who would often find the need to approach his boss with some pertinent question or other, and so allow Jane to escape from the situation.

Pat very soon settled into her job as dairymaid and Jane was very pleased to have company in some of her many jobs; they especially had fun together 'mucking-out' the cowshed and trying to push the heavy barrows full of steaming manure across the field to the heap! They quite often got stuck after days of heavy rain, but it was fun even when the thing tipped over and they had to load it all over again. It became not quite such a chore when there was someone to share the problems!

Pat told Jane she'd love to go to a dance with her next time there was one. It so happened that after the usual Friday evening queue for eggs, Tom arrived at the farm seeking out Jane. She was quick to notice that he was in a different uniform, with a single ring on the arm of his tunic, denoting that he had now become a pilot-officer. Seeing the questioning look on her face he told Jane that he'd been promoted for some weeks but had only just got his uniform. He told her that he'd come hoping that she would be free to join him at a dance in the Officer's mess the following evening. Knowing that it would now be the Officers' mess she felt a little apprehensive and asked if her land-army friend could accompany her? And since that meant she *would* go, Tom happily agreed.

Back at home, the next morning, which happened to be her day off, Jane told her parents about the invitation to the Officers' Mess, saying that she was worried about what she should wear. Her father replied, 'Well it is wartime, and uniform, if one has one, should be worn.' Jane looked downcast and said, 'Yes but Dad, our uniform is such an outdoor one, and think of the heavy brown brogues, which are our best, but not designed to dance in.'

'You should be proud of your uniform, it denotes the job you do just as your airman friend's does,' he asserted.

Jane's land-army clothes consisted of a pale yellow airtex short-sleeved shirt with a green closeknit pullover, either thick khaki corduroy breeches or light-khaki dungarees, knee-length socks and brogue shoes, a land-army tie in red, green and yellow, a light brown felt hat. Her three-quarter-length greatcoat sported a green arm-band with WLA on written in red on it, a badge showing a sheaf of corn against a green background, and a red crown on the top encircled by the words 'Women's Land Army.' All this plus sturdy Wellington boots! Hardly appropriate in an Officer's mess, Jane thought. She decided to compromise and wore her short-sleeved shirt with the badge and tie and a pair of her own green summer-weight slacks. This turned out to be perfect as Pat had done almost the same, and they both felt comfortable among the many Waafs in uniform and even a few Wrens along with two other Land girls; the latter looking very hot and bothered in their corduroy breeches, thick socks and heavy shoes. Even so, they looked quite attractive in their uniforms, and when all were introduced their dress was forgotten, the atmosphere and exchange of duties made for quite a hilarious evening.

Tom had already introduced Pat to Bob, another pilot on his squadron, and the two of them seemed to hit it off right away, just as Jane was beginning to feel that she and Tom did. It was wartime after all and 'live for the day' became everyone's motto.

24

During an interval in the dancing, Tom asked Jane a few questions about herself, where she lived and the inevitable 'had she a special boyfriend'? Her reply was, as usual, 'Yes, she had but they were just good friends and nothing more serious.' She then asked him almost the same question, and looking straight at her he told her that he had fallen in love with a certain Waaf on his last station, but things had moved on for her and he was completely over it with so many operational flights to think about now. The four of them joined up again after the buffet supper and there was plenty of talk and fun as they enjoyed the rest of the evening together. Tom was the proud owner of a small open-top car, and when the dancing finally ended he offered to drive Pat and Jane back. After the girls had made their separate plans to meet up again during the following week they parted, with Tom dropping Pat off at the farm and finally Jane back at her home.

Several days later, while Jane was in one of the fields giving 'Montgomery' some exercise on a halter on in preparation for the upcoming Agricultural Show, she was surprised to see Tom making his way over to her. 'It's my day off and as it's such a beautiful one I thought I'd like to see you in action, so to speak. Your cowman, Arthur, told me where I could find you, so here I am. Hope you don't mind!'

'Course I don't, I'm very pleased you came. Now I can introduce you to my young bull. I've looked after him since he was born, and have recently christened him 'Montgomery.' Hopefully, I will be showing him later in the year unless all agricultural shows are cancelled. Don't you think he's a fine chap?' Tom laughed at her enthusiasm, saying he hoped she'd still feel that way when he was fully grown.

He then joined Pat and Jane in the farm kitchen as they made coffee. When Mrs Freeman came in, she was able to introduce him. Her lady-boss told Tom she'd heard a lot about him and was very pleased to meet him. After their elevenses Jane took Tom to see Blackie and the other horses in the field behind the house, followed as always by the three dogs who were now the girl's constant companions. Tom asked about the farmer himself and she filled him in about his call-up to the Navy. He asked if Mrs Freeman managed everything entirely on her own. Jane told him about the nearby farmer friend who was keeping an eye on things for her, how good he was, and how all the men admired him. Although he had a very large farm himself, he still found the time to oversee this one.

Tom told Jane that he too enjoyed riding and offered to exercise the farmer's horse if her lady-boss would like him to. 'You bet she would,' Jane answered, 'he isn't getting anything like enough work and is putting on a huge belly. Let's go in and ask her.' His offer was greatly appreciated and Tom agreed to return more suitably dressed that afternoon. So began another chapter in the land-girl's life: Jane would ride Blackie, or Mrs Freeman's mare, while Tom would accompany her on 'Charlie', Mr Freeman's horse. This happened either on one of his days off or if flying was cancelled for one reason or another; then they would ride together to shut up the hens in the late evening.

The summer days of 1940 were long and mostly quite hot; very soon it was corn-cutting time and harvest began on the farm in earnest. All the Wellington bombers, Fairy Battles and other bombers had long gone from Benson Aerodrome, and it had now become a base almost entirely for Spitfires. Jane now saw little of Tom, for by this time he had joined one of the squadrons which flew from there. He had little time to talk about his flying or even telephone Jane, for the 'Battle of Britain' was well and truly underway.

Rationing in the homes was getting more acute, and the loss of friends became more and more frequent as the Battle for Britain loomed large in their future. Tom's squadron was a very secret one, and Jane knew that no questions must be asked. Even the dances on the aerodrome were cancelled, but fortunately the ones held in her village were kept going, as were the efforts of the WVS ladies, trying their best to provide food and relaxation for the many servicemen and women. When Jane and Pat could not see their young men they would play table-tennis, darts or go dancing in the village-hall, for they too needed to keep their spirits up. Once the corn was cut there was little free time for anyone on the farm and the two girls discovered the painful business of trying to stook sheaves of corn, wearing shorts to keep cool. They very soon abandoned this idea, and wore their sensible dungarees once they'd suffered all the scratches the wheat sheaves made on bare legs! The work was hard and the hours long and all for a mere twenty-eight shillings a week. The land girl's work may have been a healthy job but it certainly was one of the poorest paid. On the other hand, there really was nothing to spend one's money on, only the village hall dances or a pint in the local. There were a few small bonuses – for example, Jane's mother received an extra ration of cheese for her, and of course was in the fortunate position of getting any cracked eggs brought home by her daughter.

A break in the weather, with heavy showers and thunderstorms, brought a slight respite from harvesting, but there were many other jobs to catch up on, such as cleaning-out pens in readiness for newly born calves, the never-ending cleaning out of the chicken houses, more and more eggs to be washed, and graded for the egg- marketing board; for this was the best laying time of the year. Tom telephoned Jane whenever he could, and this he did one evening just as she was going to her bed. It was to tell her that Pat's friend Bob was being posted away to join another squadron in the South of England and that he feared he might be following him in the near future. Although she was sad for her friend she knew that this kind of thing was almost inevitable and was to be expected; it nevertheless made her realise just how fond she was becoming of her handsome pilot.

Prior to the war Jane had not been particularly interested in the

opposite sex; being with animals, especially horses, had been her main interest. Of course, she had old school boy-friends, many of whom had by this time been killed in one or other of the Forces, bringing home to her the tragedy of such young lives being lost in this terrible war. Strangely and yet sadly, just as she had been thinking of Michael, a few days later when she arrived back home from yet another long day in the harvest-field and was about to rush upstairs to soak her weary bones in the few inches of water one was permitted at this time, her Mother called her, 'Jane wait just a minute. I'm afraid we've had some bad news about Michael.' 'Oh Mum, he hasn't been shot down has he?' she asked. Her mother replied sadly, 'I'm afraid he has. He is reported 'missing in action.'
'Oh God no!' Jane cried as she sat in tears on the stairs, 'his poor Mother, what will she do?'
'Your Father has gone down to fetch her here to stay, at least until there is positive confirmation from Air Ministry. She will need her friends right now.'

Jane sobbed for a while as her mother made her a cup of tea, after which, pulling herself together, she had her bath, dressed, and rode her bicycle down to the river. The Thames was an important part of her life and had been since her childhood. It was here that she and Michael would go swimming together after school, and as she walked slowly along the river-bank, memories of times past came rushing into her mind. She tried to convince herself that he might still be alive after all.

Land girl Ch 4

Jane was very subdued for a week or two, but life had to go on, and the next time Tom rang her she told him her sad news about Michael, and said, 'This bloody war, will it ever end?' Tom tried to console her, but felt he was only making matters worse when he said that he knew full-well how she felt; he was losing chaps in his squadron almost daily.

As the darker evenings were now approaching Jane found that once more she had to cycle quite early to shut up the chickens; this was somewhat of a relief to her as it meant she had more time to enjoy her evenings. One morning, Mrs Freeman had to tell her young Land girl that very soon many of the hens would have to be sold. Such was the demand for corn that all their own crops had to be sent to 'the War Agricultural depots', and even if they could buy in corn it would be far too expensive.

Jane had to accept this explanation, although she did wonder if her job at the farm might be in jeopardy until, almost as if reading her thoughts, Mrs Freeman told her that what with the milking herd expanding, more calves arriving weekly, all the heifers in need of her care, plus the horses and the dogs, she would continue to be a great asset to the farm team, so not to give a moment's thought about not being needed. This was quite a speech and it seemed to bond them even closer. With a big smile Jane left her boss, much lighter in her own heart.

A few weeks later, with the help of Benny and Dobbin, culling-out the older hens began, and as they were being crated a lorry arrived to take them off to market. So as one chapter in her farming life approached its end, another was about to begin.

The following Friday, as the usual queue of airforce men arrived for their fresh farm eggs, Jane realised she ought to have made some sort of notice and put it up on the tree at the approach to the farm lane. Instead, she had to tell the eager young men to broadcast that there would be no more eggs for sale from now on. Most were very sympathetic, saying that they fully understood the situation; a few were almost rude to her about it, but Jane told them that none of them were half as sad as she was!

By this time in 1941, rationing of foodstuffs was really beginning to bite, for each person the allowance was: 1 fresh egg per week,
4oz bacon or ham, 8oz sugar, 2oz butter, 8oz cooking fats, one shillings worth meat, 2oz tea, 20oz jam,1oz cheese [more for farm workers]. Clothing was also rationed and each person was allowed 66 clothing-coupons which had to see them through for a year.

Now that she had more time to learn how to do other farm jobs, Dobbin asked Jane if she would like to learn to plough using two of the cart-horses. She thought this a wonderful opportunity, and thanking Dobbin for his kind thought, she readily agreed. So it was that on the next frosty morning she helped Dobbin harness Prince and one of the older horses, Bessie. Next he helped her up on the mare's back while he jumped up onto Prince, and off they rode to the field where he'd left the plough. Jane had often watched as the horses or the tractor ploughed a field and was amazed at the number of gulls and other large birds which congregated to follow the plough.

In the field they were about to plough, Dobbin hitched the two horses so that they would walk close together with the long chains from their harness attached to the plough. Jane saw right away that Prince and Bessie were quite used to the job - they knew exactly what they had to do. Dobbin walked across to the far hedge and placed sticks as markers at each end of the area to be ploughed; these would help one keep a straight furrow. Having done this, he told Jane to keep her eyes on the marker-sticks. She found that although the horses knew the drill, she needed to walk with one foot in the furrow and the other on the field-side, just as one horse would walk in the furrow as it was ploughed and the other on the field. It took her a while to get the hang of this, but as the earth was turned over by the plough she could see the sense, and the satisfaction, of cutting a truly straight furrow.

Jane loved the way each horse would give a snicker and twitch its ears as she used its name and she soon got warmed-up and exhilarated with the job. The smell of new earth as the plough turned each furrow thrilled her, and she also realised for the first time how much deeper the horse-drawn plough went compared with that pulled along by a tractor. She really became very excited about it all!

Dobbin was well pleased with her efforts when she called 'whoa' after completing her part of the field. He then helped Jane put on the horses' nose-bags which held a chaff and oats mixture for their elevenses. He too went off and sat close to the hedge where it was sheltered and proceeded to get out his own flask of tea and hunk of bread and cheese, having told Jane to go back to the farm for her own break. After finishing all her other jobs she could come back and help him finish off the field - that is 'if you can still walk after this mornin's effort!'

32

A happy but weary Land girl finally got back to the farm with the contented feeling that she'd now achieved one of the primary jobs on the farm. That same evening, when Tom arrived at her home to take her to the local hop, he found her curled-up in her father's armchair fast asleep. The effort of coping with two big horses, and walking fast behind them with one leg up and one down in the furrow had been tedious work - indeed for her it had been quite demanding. Eventually Tom decided it was time to wake her, reluctant as he was to do so. It was with a great effort that she managed to get up out of the chair. Tom was a little amused, yet proud of her grit and determination, but he also knew how much she enjoyed their evening dances. Needless to say, Jane was jolly pleased that he'd come in his car on this particular evening!

On the way to the village-hall they stopped at their usual haunt, the Castle Inn, to have a drink and meet other friends. Jane was pleased to see Deborah there with a very handsome Polish pilot whom she introduced as Pierre; he had recently arrived at the local aerodrome. When he asked Jane to dance, it happened to be a slow-foxtrot which allowed them to talk; they spoke about how he came to be in England. He told her what a terrible time his family endured as the Germans took over his country, and how he'd lost most of them. Afterwards she thought yet again how lucky she was to be working in the countryside and able to be with her family as well. The young man also told her about his friend Stazsceck, another pilot on his squadron, who had also lost every member of his family to the Nazis.

Jane then told Pierre about the other hall in the village where the WVS ladies prepared home-made meals for the forces, but 'I'm sure Deborah will tell you about it and take you there,' she added. She was later telling Tom about her talk with Pierre and once again he was pleased to know how very thoughtful she was as he knew full-well that life on an RAF operational station was anything but homely.

The year of 1941 meant that Jane would soon be 21years old, and her parents were wondering just how they could celebrate for her during these days of severe rationing. They also wondered if she really would want to celebrate with the constant loss of friends she had grown up with, and yet they felt that they simply must make some sort of effort. Meanwhile, Mrs Freeman had also realised that this important event in her Land girl's life needed to be marked, for they'd all grown extremely fond of her - this girl who would set her hand to any task asked of her, and more besides. She finally decided to see Jane's parents, and with help from Tom, Pat and Deborah plans for the occasion began to take shape.

Fortunately the birthday fell on a Saturday and the local village hall was booked for a start. Tom agreed to contact the RAF band [of which he was now resident singer], and Jane's parents and sister had lists of invitations to be sent out informing guests that there would be supper followed by dancing. The Land girl had absolutely no idea that all these preparations were being made, for she normally shunned any kind of fuss about such things as birthdays.

The morning of January 29th arrived, and Jane was amazed when she got downstairs to find parcels of all kinds. She opened those from her parents and sister first of all; they contained jodhpurs, a riding jacket and boots. She was so pleased with these, asking how on earth they had found enough clothing coupons for them. Her family's reply was, 'That is our secret, we just hope they fit'! Of course they all did, and Jane put them on right away telling her folks that she was now going for a ride on Blackie, to show them off.

It was her free weekend, and her parents breathed a sigh of relief that she was disappearing for a while as they still had more preparations to see to. Jane had told them that she and Tom would be celebrating that evening when he'd finished flying; she didn't notice the look her father gave to her mother, nor the wink he gave her sister!

Before going Jane found another parcel on the table, but she only looked at it saying she'd open it later, because the frost had almost gone and she wanted to get outside. Her father said 'just take a look inside that one on the table, Jay, as it looks most exciting.' She did just that and was thrilled to find a really good, hard, black-velvet riding hat, something she'd always wanted and needed; somehow she guessed immediately that this was from Tom. 'How did he know I'd lost mine and what is more how did he know my size?' 'He will know doubt let you into his secret later on when you meet,' her father told her, 'now be off and have a good ride, but don't fall off just to test the hat!'

The morning turned out to be perfect for riding and Blackie greeted Jane with her usual whinny, and when she rode off up the farm lane she heard, 'Happy Birthday Polly,' from Susan and Arthur, followed by 'we'll see you later,' which puzzled her somewhat. She felt smart and comfortable in her new riding kit, but it didn't deter her from taking Blackie for a good old gallop as she knew they were both in need of it. Despite the good gallop, and the fact that it was her 21st birthday, Jane couldn't help remembering the sadness of losing her childhood school friend Michael. It seemed only yesterday that he'd walked to the farm to see her; she remembered too, when she had gone to London to see him off and had a premonition that it might be the last time they'd be together.

Land girl Ch5

Going home later that morning, Jane found nobody there, so decided to make herself a sandwich. Just as she had cut the bread her parents walked in. 'Where've you two been?' she asked. 'Oh! Only down the village. Your mother and I had some people to see,' her father told her. That evening her mother said, 'Is Tom taking you somewhere special tonight?' 'I've really no idea, but yes, probably, knowing him!' Jane replied. Her mother then asked, 'Will you dress-up a bit more then?' 'What on earth can I dress-up in?' her daughter asked. 'Go up to your bedroom and maybe something will come to mind,' suggested her mother. To Jane's great surprise there was yet another parcel on her bed, quite a large one. She quickly tore off the wrapping paper and opened the box. In it she found a lovely pale-blue dress protected by tissue paper, and a note from her aunt in Lancashire wishing her a happy birthday. She was so excited she ran downstairs two-at-a-time to show her parents. 'Just look at this, and furthermore it's just my size as well, but how did Chips know that?'

'Ah well you remember the evening when you first went to the officers' mess dance with Tom and you wondered where a certain long dress had gone, I'd sent it to your aunt when she asked what she could get for your 21st birthday, and here's the answer! You should wear it tonight; I'm quite sure Tom will be taking you somewhere special.' For a girl who did not go in for dressing-up, Jane looked absolutely stunning when she finally emerged. So much so that when Tom arrived that evening he was staggered momentarily, having only seen her in riding-kit or land-army clothes. Jane noticed that he too was in his 'best-blue' officer's uniform, so, she thought, mother was right in thinking he might be taking me somewhere special on this occasion.

Therefore she was slightly, just slightly, disappointed when he stopped his car at the local village-hall. She noticed bunches of balloons hanging over the entrance. 'I wonder whatever is going on here?' she cried, and as Tom urged her forward into the main room there was a loud cheer as the band struck-up, 'Happy Birthday Jane,' and all was revealed! There were hugs from family, friends and relatives she'd not seen since the war began. And last but not least, *there* were Mrs Freeman and Susan along with Pat and all the farm workers. The latter she scarcely recognized - they were in their Sunday-best suits. All round the hall were long trestle tables which were set out for a meal, with a side buffet-table simply loaded with food and drinks.

After all the greetings had subsided, Jane's father invited everyone to sit down. He made a short speech thanking them for coming on this, his daughter's special day. He told a couple of amusing stories about her childhood, finishing by saying how proud he and Annie (his wife) were that she was doing such excellent war-work. He hoped they would all enjoy the occasion, especially the marvellous food to which so many friends had contributed. He then asked them all to 'be upstanding and drink a toast to Jane.'

Their daughter was totally taken aback - she'd had absolutely no idea that this had been planned. It was so good to see everyone - the ladies in their best war-time finery, with the men either in uniform or suits. She was too excited to eat, with Tom by her side and Pat, with Bob, who'd come some distance for the occasion. Also, there was Deborah, her land army friend with the two Polish pilots. There was so much chatter and laughter it all made a wonderful 21st birthday for her. Her father had somehow got hold of bottles of champagne and Jane made a mental note to ask how he'd managed this. Meanwhile, everyone tucked into the unbelievable feast, which was a real treat after two years of rationing. And champagne as well!

After finishing their supper with the guests, the members of the band left the table, each giving Jane a kiss on the cheek - it was time for the dancing to begin. They started by playing a quickstep, in which almost everyone joined. Tom took Jane's hand to lead the dancing and together with the 50 guests the next part of that very happy evening was enjoyed by all.

There was a huge pile of gifts waiting for her on a side table, and when she saw them she felt it was her turn to say something. As soon as the band stopped for a break, she climbed onto the stage and in a slightly wobbly voice gave her thanks to everyone for making it such a happy occasion. The evening seemed never to end, but eventually the lads in the band played 'the last waltz'. With goodnights and thanks echoing all around, the wonderful birthday celebration ended.

When Tom left her, much later, Jane found her parents having their usual bedtime drink, and putting her arms around them, she thanked them for their wonderful surprise and for all the thought and effort in organising it. She said, 'What a good thing it's Sunday tomorrow, so you can both rest! You deserve to, it's been a most wonderful birthday.'

After all the excitement, work on the farm settled down to the winter routine once more, and the trudging through snow to get to work began all over again. Now at least, Jane didn't have the hill to contend with since the few remaining hens were now in two houses just behind the farmhouse. All the animals had to be fed in their various pens; this too had its drawbacks as there was again the unenviable job of cutting the ice-cold kale from the field with hands getting red and wet, together with digging mangolds out of the clamp where they were stored; all this had to be done before feeding could even begin. Meanwhile, she had to get on with her everyday tasks and even though she was used to having sore fingers from teaching newly-born calves to lap milk from a bucket, it still was not the easiest of tasks, and required a great deal of patience and time. They were given colostrum from their mothers for the first week; this was followed by a milky solution made from powdered milk mixed in a bucket. Teaching them to drink from this meant moistening their mouths with the milk, then dipping her fingers into it; she would then put her fingers carefully them into each calf's mouth to encourage it to suck. Once the calf began to lap she would slide her fingers out. Some would learn quickly but there were always the very slow ones, and it all took time and lots of patience. After feeding them Jane took the empty buckets across to the dairy to wash them out, in 'heavenly' warm water, then after drying her hands, she massaged them with soothing lanolin, which the cowmen used on the udders of any cows with sore teats.

Her next task was the usual mucking-out of their pens and spreading dry clean straw down for their bedding. Having seen to the tiny calves it was time to feed the six-month-old ones; this feed had usually been prepared the previous day, and it consisted of rolled-oats, plus finely chopped mangolds and a very small quantity of crushed linseed, all grown on the farm.

Quite often after her elevenses Jane would tackle the horses' stables, once again spreading clean straw, and filling their hay-nets and water buckets. After this if she had the time, she would groom all three, a job she enjoyed, for they would nuzzle against her and whinny with pleasure. Often in the winter, after collecting some oats, Jane would crush them along with mangolds; then, both were mixed for the following day's feed. In the afternoon, she usually prepared the milking parlour for the afternoon's milking by hosing it all down twice, then spreading clean straw in each cow's stall. Her final job was to go across to the yard by the house, to feed the dogs and go to see Mrs Freeman for a chat and cup of tea before tackling the icy or snowy cycle home.

By this time, Jane had introduced Deborah's two Polish friends to her parents, and ever hospitable, they made them welcome at their home when they were not on duty, hoping to help make them feel part of the family. Too often, though, there was the possibility of disruption during these war days and after six happy months both boys were posted to a bomber-station in Lincolnshire. Before they left, Pierre gave Jane's father, who had himself been in the Royal Flying Corps during the 1914-18 war, a tie denoting his being a Polish pilot. Stazchek presented her mother with a pearl brooch, which had belonged to his own Mum. They had a farewell meal together, during which the two boys promised to keep in touch, and both gave Jane their usual hand-kissing as she wished them good-luck. She felt for sure they would need it.

As the lighter evenings returned once more, Jane was beginning to look forward to Tom's next visit, when the inevitable happened. Pat gave in her notice. She was moving to work on a farm nearer to Bob, and the exciting news was that they had decided to get engaged. The girls enjoyed a farewell party in their local before they parted. Mrs Freeman and Jane, with all the farm-hands, had clubbed together to buy Pat a farewell present - a gift for her 'bottom-drawer'. It was a sad parting for the girls although they'd already planned to meet again before too long.

A few days later, Arthur and Jane had a discussion with their lady-boss about getting a girl to replace Pat. They agreed that the local land-army office should be approached, so it was arranged for Jane to go into Oxford to deal with it. The following day she caught a bus into Oxford and, at the WLA recruiting office, was introduced to one of the officials, who, after shaking Jane's hand told her how pleased she was to meet her, saying, 'Are you aware that you have been selected to represent the Oxfordshire WLA to meet the Queen in London at the Dorchester Hotel?' This was a complete surprise! Jane was handed a copy of a letter which had been posted to her asking if she would be able to do this. She looked staggered and stuttered, 'O-of c-course I would, it's an honour, a- after all' but why me?,' she asked. 'You were one of the very first to enrol here when war was declared, and you have been highly recommended by your boss as well as by your farm-workers,' was the answer. 'Details are all in the letter on its way to you and we hope you will accept and have a wonderful day.' Jane stuttered her thanks, and after dealing with the matter of another dairy-maid for the farm, she made her way back to the bus-stop with a feeling of surprise and excitement..

'Did you remember to ask about another girl for us?' her lady-boss asked, smiling at the excited girl, 'I think I did, but being selected to meet the Queen came as such a shock I almost forgot why I'd gone there at all,' Jane told her boss with a laugh.

Two days later, a notification came to the farm that a new Land girl would be coming for an interview with 'the farmer'; someone from the WLA office would be telephoning about the date and time. Jane was pleased that it was all going ahead so quickly. Pat had been such a good worker and was already greatly missed. Meanwhile, Arthur reminded Jane about her friend's request when she was with them at the show the previous year, 'Good lord, I'd totally forgotten, I've not seen anything of her lately,' she told him. She talked it over with her lady-boss who told Jane that they would have to keep their word to see the girl the WLA were sending. The day and time were fixed for the interview, and when Jane went into the farmhouse for her elevenses, talking to Mrs Freeman was a pretty, fairly short, blonde-haired girl. The two girls were introduced and Jane learned that Susan had only recently finished her WLA training, and had lived all her life in London; nevertheless she seemed eager and keen to learn the job.

The weather changed dramatically with the arrival of spring; there were many more calves - most of them little heifers, and they would be added to the herd; only the bulls were sent to market for selling on. Susan had settled in very quickly and was delighted to be with animals after her time on a purely arable farm; this lightened Jane's load also, allowing her more time to exercise the horses.

One morning, Jane noticed Dobbin and Arthur laughing together as they walked across from the milking-shed and she asked what the joke was; Dobbin answered, 'When you'm got a minute Polly go and listen inside while your mate is still there, then you'll know!'

Intrigued by this, Jane did as he suggested and found Susan trying to fit the cups of a milking-machine on to Betsy's teats, the one cow which had always been difficult now that machines were used instead of hand milking. She heard 'Oh! do move over there's a darling, please move, there's a dear,' and she felt she had to put her friend right and not leave her getting nowhere with the fidgeting animal. Jane quietly said, 'Susan, try shouting at her, like 'get over damn you' or you'll be there all day with that one,' As she demonstrated a bit of farm-language to the girls both had a good laugh about it. Of course, as her friend reminded her, she had never worked with cattle before - let alone getting parts of a machine on to cows' teats.

At 5 o'clock one Sunday morning, Jane jumped out of bed, dressed quickly, grabbed a cup of milk and rushed out to get her bike. She had suddenly remembered it was her week for the early morning milking. It was one of those glorious Spring days and she felt glad to be alive. Pedalling hard, she reached the farm in double-quick time, only to meet Arthur bringing the cows in from the field, and giving her one of his looks which by now she knew so well, as he asked, had she 'had a late night'?

A bit of banter was always a good way to start the day but he was serious when he asked her to fetch in the heifer from the field behind the farm-house. 'She should calve any time today,' he added, then said, 'don't let Bess out of her kennel though, make sure she's shut in.' It was still a bit chilly so early in the day, so Jane had kept her pullover on as she ran across to get the heifer, who knew her well, for she had been one of her charges from birth. This time though, when the girl called her, she made no movement. Going closer, Jane could see then that the calf was already born and was lying at its mother's feet. As she got nearer, the tiny creature struggled to its feet and seemed to be perfectly all right, but try as she would the heifer would not begin to follow her when she called her name. Jane decided that if she were to pick up the calf and start walking out of the field, its mother would surely follow. Unfortunately, as she bent to gather the little creature up in her arms, Bess appeared, and terrified for her baby, the heifer charged at Jane.

The heifer was an Ayrshire breed, with long curving horns, and these got tangled up in Jane's jersey. She was tossed around mercilessly, until finally ridding herself of the wool, the heifer threw her to the ground. All Jane felt was a searing pain in her chest and total oblivion as everything went black. Arthur, hearing the dog barking frantically and thinking it high time both girl and heifer were across in the milking shed, ran over to the field, only to see the still form of the Land girl on the ground, together with the frightened animal guarding her calf. To his horror, he then spotted the dog. His first thought was to grab Bess and haul her out through the gate and back into her kennel.

Arthur ran to the house calling for Mrs Freeman to send for a doctor, explaining that he'd just found Jane unconscious in the field. Grabbing a blanket from an armchair, Arthur first shut the dog up then rushed back to the field to put the blanket over the girl, guessing she would be in shock. Old Benny, who had been seeing to one of the cart-horses, had heard the constant barking, and had gone over to see what was happening for himself. Between them they managed to carry Jane into the house, up the stairs and onto a bed. The doctor arrived fairly quickly and when he'd heard what had happened, he first of all examined the patient, and then asked for someone to ring 999 for an ambulance. He told them he'd seen how very close to Jane's heart the gash from the heifer's horn had gone, and said very quietly, 'I hope she's been lucky but as she is still unconscious we'd better be on the safe side and get her admitted.'

That evening, unbeknown to Jane, who was still unconscious, both her parents and Tom had been to see her. Her young man had earlier phoned to speak to Jane and had heard what had happened. Without hesitation, he requested permission to fly down to Benson to see her. Jane's parents picked him up from the airfield and they all arrived at the hospital to find that Jane was fast asleep; she had been given a sedative whilst the wound was treated. Infection was now the main worry.

A very hazy Land girl awoke the next morning wondering where she was and why. The nurse tried to fill her in, but she only vaguely knew. No one really had a concept of what had actually happened and Jane could scarcely remember herself. Later, she was examined again by one of the doctors and was advised to remain in the hospital for the next few days. The nurse agreed to phone Mrs Freeman and Jane's parents with any updates. The patient promptly went back to sleep. She scarcely felt them change the dressing on her chest, but by mid-afternoon things began to get clearer in her mind, so that by evening when Tom was again able to visit her, she saw him walking into her room carrying a bunch of scented roses and some fruit. These he quickly deposited on her bed and gently kissed her, tentatively putting his arms around her; there were almost tears in his eyes as he told her, 'You spend a lot of time worrying about me and my flying. But now I will never be sure that something like this might happen again to you. Jane, my love, please take great care.

The fact is that this has made me realise even more how very much I love you'. Looking up at him, Jane replied, 'I'm beginning to feel the same, thinking about you so much must be love. And now everything is coming back to me, so I can tell you how it all happened'. As they sat talking together, Mrs Freeman walked in, followed by the doctor who was attending Jane.

'You look better! You actually have roses in your cheeks again, but just be patient for a couple more days and with luck you'll be able to go back home,' he told her. After she'd thanked him, Jane explained to both Tom and her lady-boss exactly what had taken place in the field, 'but I still can't imagine how Bess managed to get out. I had shut her in myself.'

'The mystery was solved the next morning. When Arthur went to fetch Bess and the cows for milking, he found that Bess had burrowed under the wire-netting at one corner of her pen. 'We think that hearing you call to the heifer, instinct told Bess she should be with you,' Mrs Freeman explained. 'Oh, that would be right, she always came when she heard me, poor Bess she was really just doing her job,' Jane replied. Tom just managed *not* to say, 'poor Bess be damned'; it was only because he knew how fond she was of the dog, he managed to refrain!

Land girl ch 6

Before Jane was allowed to go back to work, she spent her days going for walks. She couldn't ride, not even her bike, and one lovely morning found herself on the old route to the hill where her chickens had been housed. The view from the hill-top was alive with blossom along the hedges, slender green corn stems peeping through in the fields, birds singing nonstop, the bleat of newly-born lambs in the fields around her, and the ewe's anxious calls if they strayed too far from them. This Spring morning, the sun was quite warm, promising a fine day, and added to the noise of birds and lambs, there came the usual sounds from the airfield below, a reminder that there really was a war on. She would not allow things to dampen her spirits, for that very morning she had had a letter from Tom giving her the long- awaited news that he was posted back again to the aerodrome near the farm. Jane decided to walk back close to the field where the older calves were grazing, and as she called to them they pricked up their ears and ran across to the fence where she was standing. It was a wonderful moment.

Next, she called in to see her lady boss to tell her the good news that she would be back at work in two days time. 'That *is* good news! You've been missed by everyone, especially the horses and dogs - even the men as they've had to double-up on many of your jobs themselves and now realise fully how much work you do. Besides all that, I've missed our chats and discussions too!' Jane stayed on for lunch at the farm and so was able to familiarise herself with what was going on. When Susan joined them, she found her friend much happier and full of all her new achievements with the animals.

The two girls met that evening. Jane's cousin had called to take her for a drink as he was home on leave from the RAF. John had been quite sweet on Deborah at one time but was especially pleased to meet the new Land girl. Gradually the pub filled with the usual airmen and WAAFS along with a few army chaps and Jane became somewhat the centre of things as many had heard of her accident. John suddenly realised that something or other must have happened to his cousin as he heard them talking, so Susan filled him in. He said it was no surprise really, for in her 'teens she had spent a great deal of time having accidents while out riding, or rather not riding! She had been thrown off horses so often when helping at the local stables exercising partially broken-in horses. He told the girl of the number of broken limbs she had had, adding, 'but it never stopped her, it's all been part of her life and I admire her for it.' One of the RAF officers asked Jane about Tom and was pleased to know that he would soon be back; 'We'll all be glad as he's a damn good pilot and extremely popular with all ranks,' he told her.

The following weekend, Tom rang to tell Jane he would be down to see her on the Sunday evening and the happy girl could scarcely wait. Her parents had a few words to say, seeing her excitement, both reminding her that he was active in the war; but nothing could dampen her spirits.

During the day Jane went to the farm to ride Blackie, just for a gentle short walk she told her boss. The whinny she got as she entered the field was music to her ears; all three of her charges were pleased to see her back, just as Jane was excited to see them. When she put the halter on Blackie the two hunters looked at her as if they were asking her to take them as well!

On that lovely Sunday afternoon she heard and saw a squadron of Spitfires taking off from the airfield. The sight of this almost lowered her spirits, so instead of the promised gentle walk, she took Blackie into one of the empty fields for a vigorous good canter which soon made her forget her worried thoughts for those flying.

In the evening, Tom arrived and after a meal and lots of chatter with Jane's parents, they decided to take a boat out on the Thames as the weather was so glorious; in no time they were amongst the many others with the same idea. It all seemed so peaceful listening to the gentle lapping of the water against the side of the boat. Jane was in a pretty blouse and shorts for a change and Tom told her how lovely she looked, so much better than the last visit when she was in hospital. He added, 'Jane, I've not forgotten what we said to each other when you were in hospital, and would like to take you to meet my family sometime soon.' Jane told him how much she would enjoy doing this, but said, 'As I've been off work and they are flat-out hay-making and rather short-handed, I'd better talk it over with my boss.' Tom said he understood her dilemma, and asked, 'Supposing I come and give a hand, and perhaps you could fix to have some leave when its finished. Do you think Mrs Freeman would agree to that?'

Mrs Freeman was very pleased to know Tom was offering to help with the hay making, for like everyone, she knew that the weather could change at any time; as she thanked him she said that once the field was cleared Jane would be free to go on leave. Furthermore, she said, 'Would it be more helpful if you stayed at the farm as one of the family, instead of trecking all the way back to the aerodrome each evening?' Tom said that he'd be most happy to take up her offer and right away went off to clear it with his adjutant and collect some of his old clothing. The following morning saw him out in the field with the other men clad in his own civilian clothes suitable for doing the job.

His help was much appreciated and he got along splendidly with everyone while Jane was busy doing her own jobs. Usually by elevenses-time she and Susan could join them, and this time both were in shorts showing off their very brown legs and generally bringing a bit of colour and banter into the field!

Jane knew that she'd need time off to fulfil her acceptance of the invitation to go to London, and Mrs Freeman assured her it would not make any difference to the leave she was about to have with Tom. Susan had already offered to do some of her work. The day arrived and fortunately the weather held good with most of the hayfield now cleared. Looking very smart, if a little hot, in her uniform, Tom drove her to catch the train to the big city, with a promise to pick her up later.

The appointed place for the land-girls to meet was at the Dorchester Hotel and as she entered, Jane saw 34 girls of all shapes and sizes, looking as hot and bothered as she felt. The train had been packed with soldiers and other forces, together with a few civilians, and it had been grimy, hot and stuffy, stopping at every small station on the way. At the appointed time, the girls were ushered into one of the hotel's lounges where cold or hot drinks were offered to each of them; also they were given instructions on what they were to do when Her Majesty arrived.

There was a sudden hush when this beautiful Lady entered the room smiling at them as they hurriedly stood up to attention. 'Girls, please relax and sit down, this is to be an informal meeting. I am just so pleased to see and meet you all. But first of all, do take off your pullovers and hats and be comfortable, I'd very much like to talk to each one of you in turn and afterwards we will have tea.'

Queen Elizabeth listened with interest as each girl described her own farm work; it seemed that each one was doing something different. Jane was amazed at the variety: some worked on a farm with a gang of other land-girls, some were on purely arable farms with no animals at all, others were in forestry or on market gardens, and others were loners on a dairy farm, as Jane had originally been.

Tea was simply wonderful, as most of the girls had not seen dainty sandwiches and cream cakes for many a long day, and all felt free to tuck-in. Her Majesty was very interested in all their activities, including their off-duty ones. She had such an easy-to-talk-to way, and smiled a great deal, making each one of them feel *special*. They almost didn't want the interview to end. But of course it did, with a firm handshake for every girl, and Her Majesty's grateful thanks for what they were doing whilst their country was at war. When she had gone, they all felt that nothing in their lives would ever be the same again. What a wonderful lady.

Having said their goodbyes to each other, the girls were taken to their various stations. Each and every one of them felt ready to tackle whatever job they were called upon to do – their visit had been such a boost to their morale. Tom met Jane at the station as promised and told her, once she stopped talking and allowed him to get a word in, that he'd been riding the two hunters for most of the day, so his conscience was clear about taking her away for a few days. Dropping her off at her home, he arranged to pick her up the following morning. After taking her in his arms and kissing her long and hard he drove back to the airfield. The first thing Jane did was to tell her parents about her lovely day; then she rang Mrs Freeman with her news and made sure all her jobs would be covered in her absence; once assured about this, she finally felt that all was well for her first short holiday.

Driving towards Dorset in the open-topped car was heavenly, and knowing that they could be together for an entire week's leave made it all seem perfect. Tom's parents lived in a small village a few miles from Poole, adjacent to a lovely stretch of the coastline; he told Jane how much he wanted to take her walking, and that there was so much here he wanted to show her. Just as they pulled into the drive to his parents' house, a young man with blonde hair greeted them. Tom asked, 'What the devil are *you* doing here, I thought you were still in Canada training?' He replied, 'Well, yes I was and now, as you see I'm back, and boyoh! it's jolly good to see you. This must be Jane. Mum said you were bringing a girl-friend home with you.' Holding out his hand, he told her, 'I'm Nigel, Tom's brother. It's great to meet you Jane.'

The boys' parents, Mr and Mrs Gregory, suddenly appeared, and there were smiles all round as Tom introduced them to Jane. The couple were obviously overjoyed at having both their sons with them, and welcoming the girl to their home, told her that she was the first land-army girl they had actually met. Mr Gregory told them how excited his wife had been when he heard they were coming, adding 'she's been cooking ever since.' After they'd had coffee, Mrs Gregory took Jane upstairs to the room she'd made ready for her visit. It was just as pretty as Jane had imagined it would be, after seeing the ground floor, and the view from the bedroom was quite breathtaking. 'No wonder Tom said he wanted to take me for lots of walks,' Jane said, 'you are so fortunate living around here - the war seems very far away, it's so peaceful.'

She went on to tell Mrs Gregory about the farm and her work there, how she and Tom had met, about her own parents and where they lived. She felt really at home and could have chatted longer when suddenly a voice called, 'Have you two gone to sleep or something?' It was Tom, anxious that they didn't waste a moment of their short time here, and told Jane he wanted to take her to meet someone very special. 'If that's okay with you, mother, I want her to meet grandma.' 'Try to be back for lunch unless she presses you into staying. You know how lonely she gets. Meanwhile Nigel can give me a hand!'

After walking through the pretty village they came to a charming old thatched cottage, with a pretty garden in front. On opening the door Tom called out, 'Are you there grandmother-of-mine?' A small voice replied, 'No, I'm out hunting, you young rascal, but pleased I am that you've come along to see me so soon.' They walked through the old-beamed cottage into the back garden, where Jane noticed border upon border full of summer flowers. On the lawn, in the shade of an old apple tree, was Tom's gran, sitting in a deck chair with a cat on her knee. As she looked up and saw them she struggled to get up but Tom reached her first and throwing his arms around her cried, 'Are you all right grandmother?' The smile of joy on her face told him she'd only been dozing as she kissed him fondly. Tom introduced Jane and kissing the girl's cheek, grandma told her she'd heard from her daughter-in-law that Tom was bringing a lady-friend to stay, and how very pleased she was to see them. As the three of them went into the cottage, Tom gave his grandmother a helping hand - he could see that her old legs had got quite crippled since his last visit.

Jane was delighted with everything she saw, both inside and out, telling the old lady, 'You have a simply lovely place here. It's not only ancient but beautiful as well.' 'Thank-you dear, I've lived most of my life here except when I was young like yourself; then I was in the first world war serving in the Royal Flying Corps. I rode a motorbike as a dispatch-rider. Sadly now both my grandsons are in yet another war.' Jane, having noticed by then how very frail she was, asked, 'Do you live alone here?' 'I do dear except for my cat and an old pony which the boys rode when they were younger. I have a lad in the village who comes to do the garden but sadly I expect he'll be called-up any time now.' Jane followed her into the kitchen, for she had asked them both to join her in a cup of cocoa. The walls and ceiling were white in contrast to the stone-flagged floor, and there were many old beams in the ceiling. Jane fell in love with the place as well as with Tom's kindly grandmother, who obviously doted on her grandson.

Suddenly, right out of the blue, grandma asked Tom, 'Well, are you planning to marry this girl?' Jane was taken aback at this direct question and made a hasty retreat into the garden. Tom eyed his grandma steadily, 'If she'll have me, I will.' Then his grandmother sighed and said, 'Though not while this war's still on. We've got too many lonely young widows in this village, and heaven forbid that anything should happen to make her one as well.' To that Tom replied, 'Gran! I've not even popped the question yet, and if the answer is yes, then we'll just remain engaged until I've finished operational flying. Will that be okay with you?' 'Just you come through this war safely and be here for my 90th birthday, both you and Nigel, that's all I ask,' were her final words.

After a while, Tom told her, 'Grandma, we must get back or mother will be getting fidgety about lunch, and Nigel wants us all to go for an early drink with him to celebrate his homecoming. We'll be along again some time tomorrow'. With that, he planted a kiss fondly on her forehead and headed for the door. Jane had been outside admiring the garden when he called her. 'I must say goodbye to your gran and will be with you in a jiff.' She found the old lady had dozed off, and not wanting to waken her, she simply gave her a fond peck on the cheek and touched her bony old hand. 'What a wonderful lady your gran is - so very different from mine, who is a religious fanatic, though a nice one!' Jane told Tom.

They wandered back to his parents' house holding hands, feeling so happy just being together. Before going in, Tom turned and took Jane in his arms saying, 'I really meant what I said to grandmother just now. If you agree, I'd love us to get engaged and hopefully marry once the war is over.' 'Is this a proposal?' Jane asked, 'if so, may I think about it? I do love you Tom, but it's such a worrying time right now, perhaps we should talk it over first.' Tom understood. They'd not known one another very long, and had scarcely spent much time together until now. 'Let's go in and see what everyone is doing,' he said.

They spent a very jolly evening together, and during dinner

Nigel asked Jane if she'd mind if he and Tom went sailing the next day as this was something they had always done together. 'That is if we can still get a boat and are still allowed to get down to the sea with all the barbed-wire along the shore-line'. Jane replied saying she thought she would go along and spend more time with their grandmother, unless Mrs Gregory had anything else planned.

After she'd helped with the breakfast dishes the next morning there seemed nothing more to do, so Jane asked Tom's mother if she was coming along with her to see Gran. She told her, 'Just a bit of the way - there's some shopping I must do and I'm sure she'll be delighted to have you all to herself!'

They parted near the village shop where many people spoke to them, asking Mrs Gregory about her sons. Jane walked on down to the lovely cottage where she found a young man busily weeding one of the flower beds; standing up he told her, 'She's expecting you Miss, you'll find her in the conservatory.' Jane thanked him and went inside. The old lady looked much perkier and, greeting her with a hug, told Jane they could settle down as she wanted to hear more about her, her land work and how she and Tom had met. 'I want to know everything. It's a long time since I've had a young lady to chat to.'

Afterwards, having answered all Gran's questions, Jane was given a tour of the cottage. While they were in Gran's bedroom, the old lady put a small package into Jane's hand, asking her not to open it until she got home. "My husband gave that to me before he went off to fight in the last war and now I'd like you to have it. Enjoy the rest of your leave with my grandson, and I'll keep praying for his safety, for yours, and for Nigel's - and please be happy while he is still with you.' Jane left almost in tears, and wondered if she said 'yes' to being engaged, Tom would feel happier. She knew she dearly loved him and maybe he needed to know she'd be there for him.

Later that day, she remembered the gift grandma had put into her hand; she'd popped into her pocket. Jane opened the little box, and, lying there on cotton-wool was a beautiful ring with a large emerald stone. Slipping it on her finger, Jane was amazed to find that it was an almost perfect fit, and so very lovely. I really can't accept this, was her first thought. I must talk to Mrs Gregory about it. When she found her, she produced the ring, telling her hostess what had taken place and how awkward she felt now that she'd seen it. 'Well you mustn't. She always said that she wanted to give it to whichever of her grandsons first became serious about a girl, especially if she approved their choice, which she obviously has. Keep it and enjoy wearing it with our blessing.' Jane said, 'I've never had a ring before, I don't wear any jewellery, let alone a beautiful piece like this, but I do feel very honoured that grandma chose to give it to me.'

The next day was warm and sunny once again, and she and Tom made a picnic-lunch and set off to walk along the coast. Nigel had declined their offer to go with them, much as he would have liked to; it was obvious to him that Tom was very smitten, and he and Jane needed time together. He told his parents that it was a good thing Tom had seen Jane first, 'If I had, he wouldn't have stood a chance!' His mother looked fiercely at him but decided not to say anything, although she had observed Nigel looking at Tom's girl more than once.

Meanwhile, the two hikers had reached the Purbeck area which

Jane thought amazingly beautiful even with all the barbed-wire around the lovely bays below. They managed to find a shady spot to sit and eat their lunch. Tom had even discovered a bottle of white wine in the sideboard at home, and with his penknife tried in vain to open it; his Land girl was more ingenious, and her hands were somewhat tougher than his! She finally got it open, only to discover they'd no glasses to drink it from, so with much laughter they passed the bottle back and forth to each other. The sandwiches tasted wonderful, even though they contained the usual boring wartime Spam; nothing could spoil this day for them. They lay back on the grass, looking up at the deep blue sky, both feeling utterly contented. Suddenly, a squadron of bombers flew over, bound for Germany probably. 'Why did they have to come and spoil our day'? Jane muttered. 'Just to remind us not to be too happy I guess,' Tom replied, remembering just what lay ahead for him after this leave.

When Jane and Tom went to the local that evening with Nigel, who for some reason had decided to over-indulge that evening, there were a few of his old pals in the pub and he went across to play cards with them. Tom suddenly realised his brother was at the bar a little too often and suggested to Jane that they went home. She thought that they ought to tell Nigel they were off, but Tom, knowing his brother, said, 'He's happy, let us just leave.' Later that night there was a commotion outside her room as a somewhat inebriated young man tried to open the door to his room. She felt rather sorry for him; he had finished his pilot's training and was about to embark on flying bombers, and seemed far too young for such a responsible position.

Nigel was due back in Lincolnshire the following day, but his appearance at the breakfast-table told the story of the previous evening; he scarcely spoke, and when he did it was only to his parents. He informed them that he was going to see his grandma and would be back for a bite of lunch before leaving. Jane offered to go with him as Tom had other things to attend to. She tried making conversation but only got, 'Sorry about last night, hope I didn't spoil your evening.'

They went into the cottage together to see his gran, who again was pleased to see them. After asking Jane where Tom was, Gran turned to Nigel saying, 'I hoped you'd come. I know this is the last day of your leave and soon Tom and Jane will be leaving also.' Jane told her, 'We will be along together before we go. Right now, may I go and look around the garden? It's so lovely and I want to be able to remember it all.'

After lunch with the family, Nigel was ready to leave. He had already said his goodbyes to both parents, who were understandably upset. Tom was taking him to the station and picking up some of his brother's kit, went out to his car. Suddenly Jane felt Nigel's arms around her holding her as though he would never let her go. It was a little embarrassing for her hearing him say, 'My brother is a lucky devil to have such a lovely girl as you. Be good to him and God bless you both.' In reply, as she got over the shock, Jane gave him a kiss on the cheek telling him to take care and that she wished him lots of luck. She promised to make sure Tom was happy. It was quite an emotional parting, and she felt the tears stinging her eyes, knowing full-well the danger he would soon be in.

All too soon, their leave also came to an end, but Jane felt very much part of Tom's family and promised to visit again whenever she could.

Land girl Ch 7

They were lost in their own thoughts as they drove back. Suddenly, Tom pulled into a lay-by and, stopping the car, put his arms around Jane and proceeded to kiss her firmly on the mouth as though he were telling her that she belonged to him alone. They remained there without speaking for a while until, with a big sigh, the young man started up the engine and they continued their journey. On reaching Jane's home, Tom kissed her again before telling her he'd ring as soon as he possibly could after seeing what his next movements were. Jane, although feeling very happy after such a lovely few days with Toms' family, felt the tears coming into her eyes as he drove away.

Back at the farm once more, she found that all her jobs had been taken care of in her absence. Arthur was the first to tell her she'd been well and truly missed, especially by Bess who would not even leave her kennel and apparently had eaten very little. He and Dobbin had looked after the horses between them, but even they'd played up whenever he'd ridden them. Eventually he got round to asking if she had had a good time; this brought a smile to Jane's face as she enthused about her holiday. She told him she would go and get Bess right away and sort her out first. Arthur reminded her that 'Monty' needed exercising: 'Your mate, Susan, tried to handle him but he was having none of that'!

Jane went straight across to let out the dogs and could scarcely breathe as they covered her with their licking, then ran around her until she'd given them their food; then she had to shut them in their kennels to get into the farmhouse and report to her lady boss. Mrs Freeman was alone in the kitchen and, seeing her

Land girl back safe and sound, was almost as delighted as the dogs had been. 'We have all missed you Jane, I don't think any of us had realised just how much work you put into each day, until you weren't here, and it's been some job covering everything; but have you enjoyed your break and meeting Tom's family?' Jane spent quite a while telling her about the trip to Dorset and the family, and finally said she was pleased to be back with her beloved animals. 'Come and tell me more during your elevenses and tell me what Tom is doing now. All the men told me how marvellous he was helping with the hay and doing all your jobs when you went up to London.'

So the year of 1941 came towards its end with news of more and more bombing at home and over Germany. Food rationing became even tighter; at the farm they enjoyed a good harvest thankfully, and so the winter days began to set in once more. Her friend Deborah had seen a great deal of her Polish pilot, Pierre, whenever he got some leave, but, like Jane, she lived with the constant fear of bad news.

In December, came the terrible news of the Japanese bombing Pearl Harbour. The loss of life was staggering. There was also the loss of many ships. The one good thing that came out of it was that *at last* the Americans were forced into the war and proceeded to come over in thousands as allies of the British Forces - in the air, on the sea and in the army. Everyone went around singing 'the yanks are coming' while others thought it *'about time.'*

Jane and Deborah met some of the Americans first of all when they were at one of the village dances. The forces were based only about four miles away at a place known as Mount Farm.

They were a jolly crowd, most not having experienced war-time conditions before, but things were soon to change for them. Many were pleased to receive homely hospitality, to which they always contributed, not being rationed as their English friends were. Jane's parents were able to offer hospitality to some, and in fact her sister Kathleen became very friendly with one 'master sergeant' called Dusty whose home was in Indiana.

Before that, the Christmas period had occasioned many discussions and plans about who would be working and when. Jane had decided right away that as she'd only recently had some leave she would be one of those on duty; Arthur agreed to join her.

Mrs Freeman had already told them that she would be going away to spend time with relatives, and on the evening of her departure Jane discovered a note on the kitchen table wishing her a Very Happy Christmas; with the note were several parcels with her name on. It was now Christmas Eve, so she decided to leave opening them until the following morning as she was staying in the farmhouse as 'house-sitter' for her lady boss.

Just then there was a knock on the door, and on opening it, Jane was surprised to see Tom already dressed in his best blue uniform. 'I wanted to wish you a Happy Christmas, and guessed you might be on your own here tonight, so came along.' 'Am I pleased to see *you*! I was just about to make myself something to eat so we can eat here together if that's okay with you?' Tom hesitated a moment before asking, 'Do you have to stay for any reason or could you come to the Mess with me? There will be a buffet supper with dancing to follow.'

'That sounds good fun,' replied Jane, 'but the thing is I have some presents to deliver; if we could do that first, then I'd love to come with you. I have to go to Arthur's, then down the village to Frank's to meet his family, and finally to see Benny in his cottage which is the farthest one down in the village.' Tom agreed to help her do all this, telling her there was no rush to get to the Mess. He realised how keen Jane was to do her 'Father Christmas' act. He hadn't been able to give her any prior warning about this evening as they'd been extra busy on the camp; he'd just come on the off-chance that she would even still *be* there let alone be pleased to go with him to the party. It was fortunate that he'd come in his car as this would make their delivery job much quicker.

Later, as they began delivering the presents, they got somewhat delayed at the first two stops. There were excited children to be hugged and drinks being offered. At Benny's cottage, he welcomed them, still puffing away on his old pipe, and insisting that they sat down in front of his log fire while he fetched some of his 'own brew' in order to toast them both. Jane got so warm and comfortable as Tom chatted to Benny that she almost fell asleep. Suddenly she felt an arm lifting her out of the old chair as Tom said, 'We really must be off,' and as she sleepily gave the package of precious tobacco to Benny she told him, 'This is not just because it's Christmas, it's for all the times you've helped and been there for me since I came to the farm.' With that she kissed Benny on the cheek, and as they left, one pretty lonely old man felt just a mite less alone as he called out, 'God bless the pair on ee.'

Once back at the farm, Tom said he'd take the dogs for a run while Jane had a bath and dressed in her party gear. As he walked back into the room she told him how strange it felt being in girlish finery instead of dressed as a farm labourer. Her boy-friend, looking hard and lovingly at her, said, 'Jane, I can't tell you just how much meeting you has meant to me, *is meaning to me*, and how I love your generous giving nature, in fact how much I love everything about you.' After that little speech there were many embraces and kisses before they finally set off to the party.

Their arrival coincided with the band breaking off for the buffet, and what a grand spread it was, complete with a huge Christmas cake and port-wine to drink with it. To her surprise, Tom went on the stage with the band later and sang some beautiful songs, some especially for Jane. While she was dancing with Tim, a friend from the squadron, he told her, 'Yes I *was* right, I thought our Tom was smitten with a local Land girl! Now I'm sure of it and suspect *that girl is you*, am I right?' Jane's blushing cheeks rather told their own story and Tim observing this told her, 'He's a lucky fellow that's all I can say. Jolly good luck to you both.'

Tom, rejoining Jane as Tim went back on the stage, said what a good buddy he was and a great cornet player in the band as well. 'You didn't tell me you could sing like that - it was simply wonderful and made me feel very special' she told Tom, 'Oh, but you are, especially to me and my family, and I'm sure to everyone on the farm as well,' was his reply. All too soon, it was the last waltz and all the way through it Tom sang the romantic tune, 'falling in love again' to Jane. As it ended, he bent his head and kissed her long and hard on the mouth On the drive back to the farm, he produced a small package out of his pocket saying, 'Happy Christmas, my love, and I'll ring you in a day or two. I'm off home early tomorrow for my Christmas break, and

hopefully this will be the last one we have to spend apart.'
Jane was somewhat stunned, for Tom had not mentioned going
down to Dorset to her before. She still managed a shaky, 'Drive
carefully, and I wish *you* a Happy Christmas, and the same to all
your family, but I can't help wishing I was coming with you.'

Still feeling in a romantic mood Jane found it impossible to
sleep, going over and over the events of the evening. She knew
full well that she felt the same as Tom, yet the terrible war was
still there, coming between them all the time. In the end, she
gave up and went downstairs to get herself some cocoa, and as
she was drinking it she suddenly realised that it was now
Christmas Day. Seeing Tom's package where she'd left it on the
table, Jane opened it and found a most beautiful gold locket. On
a card was written, 'Jane with *all my love*'.

Realising how fast their relationship had moved on Jane felt full
of remorse. She had given no thought to buying a present for
Tom. Suddenly very tired, she gave in and went back to bed,
thankfully falling immediately into a deep sleep. In no time, she
heard a voice in the distance calling, 'Polly are you alive and
up?' Realising it was Arthur and that the day had already begun
she dressed hastily. Pulling on her boots, went across to let out
the dogs; then fed the horses with their hay and oats and finally
arrived in the cowshed to find that Arthur had already washed all
the cows' udders prior to milking them. Shouting out, 'Happy
Christmas Arthur,' she quickly got stuck into her job. When
milking was well under way he came up to her saying, 'You
look rosy this morning, did you go out with your fella last night?
The missus thought you might feel lonely, with it being
Christmas Eve an' all, so she came over to fetch you but found
no one in.' 'Yes. Tom came down and we went to a party in the

Mess, and it was quite late finishing,' she replied. Putting a friendly arm across her shoulder, Arthur said, with a twinkle in his eye, 'I'll bet it was! I well remember those days meself, but remember to keep your feet well on the ground Polly, he's a fighter pilot after all and this blasted war still rages on. Oh, I nearly forgot - my missus wants you to join us for dinner at about two o'clock, and she won't take no for an answer!'

The Christmas dinner turned out to be a lively family affair with fourteen sitting down to eat the huge meal. Jane guessed that Arthur's wife had been saving coupons for a long time to produce such a feast. She naturally helped with the clearing and washing-up, and after thanking them all, she left. She wanted to phone her own parents and to get some of her other jobs done before it was time for the afternoon milking.

At the house, all the parcels were still on the table. There were presents from her own family, and from Pat, Susan and Mrs Freeman. The latter was a blue and white checked shirt and blue tie with a gold riding-crop brooch pinned to it. Jane paused for a moment hoping that all the gifts she had given were appreciated as much as these to her were. A land-girl's pay of 28 shillings a week did not leave much for present buying, as her food and keep had to be deducted from this; on the other hand, there wasn't a lot to spend one's money on in wartime either.

The Christmas break over, Susan returned and the two girls had much to talk over. The weather was not too severe and Jane was able to drive the tub-cart or ride out on Blackie, exercising the dogs at the same time, while Susan went back to being the dairymaid once more.

Once Mrs Freeman was back, Jane took her out several times in the tub-cart finding her completely at ease controlling Blackie, and therefore able to get around to do her shopping. Jane could now have her own four-day leave, which she was spending with her parents and sister. Before going, she phoned the Mess and luckily Tom was found and they were able to talk. Jane so much wanted to thank him for his wonderful present, and to make arrangements to meet as soon as she got back. She sensed some hesitation from Tom but he assured her, 'it was just pressure of work'.

Jane's parents were in their early 60s, and both very busy people. Her father had his own building business and was also he was at this time engaged on 'river patrol', fire-fighting duties; in addition, he served on several committees. Her mother was in the Women's Voluntary Service, the Women's Institute and also served on other committees. Furthermore, she was clerk to the local Parish Council. Her sister, Kathleen, lived at home with them but travelled daily to a local factory where parts for Spitfires were made, and where she was secretary to the boss.

Her first evening at home was full of lively chatter, with everyone catching up with each other. It was not until bedtime that Jane found the opportunity to tell them how serious things had become between herself and Tom. Both her parents had served in the RFC (Royal Flying Corps) during the first world war, and therefore understood how easy it was to start a romantic affair in wartime; both felt slightly worried hearing this news.

The following morning, Jane decided it was time she visited her cousins who lived just along the road. She discovered that luckily both were home on leave from the RAF and so they had plenty of catching up to do. John, her older cousin, asked her if she would join them the next evening at the 'Young Farmers' New Year's Eve Ball.' Having said she'd love to, Jane suddenly realised that this was an evening-dress affair and that she only had her 21st birthday dress; this didn't quite fill the bill for a ball. Right away, her aunt, seeing her hesitation, told her that she was visiting her hair-dresser in town the following morning and would love to take her shopping.'Let it be a late Christmas present from your uncle and me!' An excited Jane said that she had plenty of clothing coupons to use, for she lived mostly in her land-army clothes, and there and then the shopping trip was fixed for the next day.

Once they'd got to Oxford, it was good to see that there were nice clothes still available, despite wartime shortages and coupons. Jane found a lovely, pale blue long dress with tiny pink rosebuds stitched on it. It suited her colouring well. Looking at the price she was a little worried about her aunt spending quite so much on her; she asked the shop-owner if she would keep it for her while she fetched her aunt. Once her Aunt Dora had seen the dress on her niece, she had no hesitation in footing the bill. Jane looked beautiful. Much later, when Jane was dancing in her new dress and so thoroughly enjoying herself, the good lady felt that it was worth every penny!

There were many faces that Jane recognised at the ball, and amongst them was her friend Deborah. Although many were strangers, the two girls were never alone or without a dancing partner. Things livened-up considerably as it neared midnight with the arrival of 1942, and unused as she was to alcohol and late nights, Jane suddenly felt very weary. She found herself missing Tom dreadfully; nevertheless she continued to join in the revelry, fearing that many of these faces would probably not be around by next year.

Her cousin obviously realised how late it was all of a sudden, and walked over to ask Jane if she was ready to go home. She had to admit that she was, telling him what a great evening it had been. Together they set off through the almost deserted village. In her bedroom later, taking off her lovely dress, Jane thought wistfully, 'I wonder when I'll ever wear this again.'

The usual bright and cheerful girl finally got down to breakfast late the next morning, and answered all her mother's questions almost mechanically. She also told her parents how for some reason the evening had brought home to her just how dreadful things really were in this war, particularly for all the young men. It was then that Jane told them how lucky she felt, living and working in the country - even though they had had a bomb dropped in one of the fields a little while ago.'Good lord! You didn't tell us about that,' her mother cried anxiously. Jane's reply was, 'Oh it was nothing to worry about, but just enough to make us remember that we are, after all, very close to a fighter airfield'.

Land girl Ch 8

One evening some weeks later, as they were walking down to the village, Tom told Jane that if he were posted he wouldn't want her to give up her job on the farm, for he knew how much she loved it and how fond she was of Mrs Freeman. 'But let's not think about it now,' he said, 'just take each day as it comes, and enjoy our time together.' It turned out to be quite some time before these words Tom had just spoken really registered with Jane.

The weeks of the winter of 1942 went by and soon springtime was beginning to feel almost like summer as everything everywhere began to change. The view from the hilltop was very different now: there was blossom on the hedgerows, the corn was showing through well in the fields, and joyful birdsong mingled with the distant sound of aero engines from the airfield below. The latter was the only thing that marred Jane's ride out on Blackie. But to compensate, there was the bleating of the lambs in the nearby fields, with their mothers' anxious calls when they strayed any distance away from them.

The morning sun was really quite warm and the dry air and cloudless sky promised a fine day. Yet again, Jane felt how fortunate she was as she and Blackie made their way back to the farm. For some reason, probably because of her own contentment in her job, she thought of Deborah, and how, at the New Year's ball, she'd told her how unhappy she was on the farm where she worked. Now Jane decided to try and do something about it just as soon as she could. She noticed how the grass had grown in the fields and thought maybe some of her older calves could soon be let out, and as though reading her mind, Arthur was waiting to tell her she could do just that.

By now it was time for elevenses and in the house she found her lady boss reading a letter; she looked up and told Jane that her husband was due home on leave the following week, and asked her to give his two hunters a good curry-combing, for she'd noticed that their winter coats were beginning to come off. Jane said she'd see to this as soon as she had helped with cleaning out the yard, telling her boss, 'It's got very high where the young stock have been wintering.' 'Do you think you should be doing that heavy job so soon after your accident? I know your ribs are still sore.' In the end, it was Dobbin who offered to do the heavy shifting of the soggy manure when he saw her trying valiantly to do it, but still looking somewhat tentative.

The next morning, over their cup of tea, Mrs Freeman discussed with Jane about getting another Land girl, or she wondered, should she wait a while to hear if Pat had settled down in Lincolnshire. Jane had offered to help Susan out in the dairy as long as some of her own jobs were covered, but finally they decided that they should apply for another dairy girl forthwith. It was then that Jane was able to mention Deborah: 'We don't need to apply for any other Land girl - I promised Deborah that should such an occasion arise we would let her know. Although she has never actually worked with cows I'm sure she will soon learn.' So the arrangements for extra help were set in motion.

The imminent arrival home of Mr Freeman had everyone on the farm making sure all was 'in apple-pie' order: places were cleaned out that had been left untouched, every animal's bedding was refreshed, his horses' coats shone in the spring sunshine and all seemed in perfect readiness; that is, until the evening before his arrival. When Jane called in at the farmhouse to say she was off home, as she usually did, it was to find Mrs Freeman halfway up the stairs looking in absolute agony and scarcely able to speak. Apparently, she had been riding her own mare, which had not been seriously ridden for quite some time, but wanted to show her husband how well she could manage her now. It seemed that the mare had thrown her off on the hard tarmac road when a large lorry drove past and spooked her. As she fell, her already damaged leg, the one with the iron on, had got stuck in the stirrup and she'd been dragged quite some way before the mare calmed down and stopped so that Mrs Freeman could get free.

Having done that, she still had some distance to go before reaching home. Still holding on to her horse she was almost dragged along, and now was in dreadful agony and barely conscious. Jane helped her as best she could up to her bedroom, and once she'd got her onto the bed she rushed down to telephone for the doctor. Remembering how sweet tea had once helped her, Jane made her a cup right away. Next she ran to get Arthur and they stayed with Mrs Freeman until the doctor arrived. The three of them managed to get the badly damaged iron splint off her leg. The doctor said, 'It will need to be x-rayed, so I will ring for an ambulance. I trust one of you will be able to go along with her?' Naturally Jane wanted to go in the ambulance with her lady-boss and as Arthur had finished the milking, she was able to get him to deal with the mare and her other chores. Before leaving in the ambulance, she remembered to say to him, 'You must be here when Mr Freeman arrives if I'm not back, and tell him what has happened.' She went to pack a few necessary items for Mrs Freeman as she guessed that it might mean a stay in the hospital. In the ambulance, Jane saw that the patient was fast asleep, having succumbed to the sedative given to her by the doctor. What a homecoming for her husband!

The prognosis after the x-ray was that the leg had been severely twisted and an operation would be necessary as soon as it could be arranged. By this time Mrs Freeman was awake, and although still in great pain, managed to say, 'What a homecoming for John. Whatever will he say and how will he manage?' In her usual practical way, Jane told her not to worry, someone would look after him. She must concentrate on getting better.

A day or two later, once he'd got over the shock of finding his wife in a hospital bed instead of at home, Mr Freeman heard from Jane all about the new Land girl. 'Well, you are certainly a good organiser as well as everything else. My wife has nothing but the highest praise for all you do, and I really do thank you Jane. When do we expect Deborah to arrive, and where is she going to live?' he asked. 'Oh it's all organised - nothing for you to worry about. She will have digs with Arthur and his family for the time being,' Jane told him.

The operation on Mrs Freeman was most successful and after two weeks she was home, albeit on crutches for a while. Everyone on the farm did all they could to make things easier for both she and her husband. Mr Freeman only had two weeks' leave, but even this was curtailed when one morning he heard that there was additional urgent need for convoys to be protected. He was recalled.

One evening, two weeks after Lt Cdr Freeman's recall, just before Jane was leaving the farm for her cycle home, she was called into the house to answer a phone call from Tom; 'As it's such a lovely warm evening, I wondered if you'd bring along your swimming togs and we could take a boat out, then find somewhere to eat along the river-bank. How does that idea sound to you?' Jane's reply was simply, 'It sounds heavenly and I'll be ready when you call.'

Jane put on her one and only summer-dress, gathered the necessary swimming things and was ready the moment she heard Tom peeping his car horn. She was quite excited as it had been a long time since the weather had been warm enough for an evening swim in the Thames. Tom thought how lovely his girl looked in her yellow gingham dress over her already sun-tanned body and the fringe of her hair was blonded by the sun. Meanwhile, Tom was thinking, 'god, I'm going to feel like hell later on when I have to tell her my news'.

Before they set off Tom asked after Mrs Freeman. Jane replied, 'I thought she was coping very well but when I looked in this afternoon she quickly put down a letter she'd been reading and her face looked quite pale.'

Tom did his very best to ensure that they spent an almost magical evening together. They were using a motor-launch belonging to one of his officer friends, cruising slowly along the river looking for a well-known spot where one could swim. There Tom took Jane in his arms telling her again just how much he loved her. They changed into their swimming things and dived into the clear water where both enjoyed some underwater swimming before racing out to get dry. By now they were feeling quite hungry and in an instant Tom started up the cruiser's engine and with one hand holding Jane while he steered with the other, he broke into song - a love song that he knew his girl would wish to hear: 'If you were the only girl in the world'. Quite soon they reached a landing-stage and there across a lawn were tables and chairs, all looking very inviting and all with gaily coloured umbrellas. 'Ah! this is where we are going to have supper', Tom told her as he helped her out onto the bank. 'But whatsay we go inside first and look at a menu and then, if you'd like to, we'll eat outside, it's so lovely here by the river. Inside, Jane was amazed to see so many young men and women in their various uniforms, but all cheerful and seemingly having such good fun. It was a tonic to see.

Tom went to the bar to get their drinks and could scarcely believe his eyes when he saw Jane talking away to a young soldier as if she knew him. Looking somewhat flushed, she introduced him to the young sergeant: 'Can you believe it Tom, this is Bill who I knew *long ago* when I worked down in Somerset - in fact, when we were both seventeen. He tells me he's one of the lucky ones to have returned alive from the shambles that was Dunkirk.' The two young men shook hands, then Tom asked the soldier how he recognised Jane again after all these years. He replied, 'You don't forget a girl like this one! The smile was, and still is, unforgettable. We were good pals then, although those days seem a lifetime ago now.' Tom asked him if he was okay after his ordeal on those beaches. 'Physically I'm fine but I had a long spell in hospital and still get the occasional bad nightmares, hearing the screaming and seeing the boatloads of friends disappear as their boats were hit. But you two are not here to listen to me, and I just want to wish *you* the very best of luck. Jane has told me what you do, and I'm so glad to have met up with you both.'

Having ordered their meal, they talked about the coincidence of meeting Bill; and thereafter only the things that millions of young lovers talk about when they are together. The whole evening was a memorable one for them: the good food and the companionship of all those around them. They cruised back along the almost silent river with Jane saying she hoped they'd be able to do this again soon. Fortunately she didn't notice Tom with his fingers crossed as he said, 'Very soon I hope.' He started to sing again as they went along and this time it was, 'We'll meet again, don't know where, don't know when,' and it seemed very poignant, for when he'd finished the song he gathered Jane in his arms saying, 'I've been dreading spoiling our lovely evening, but I have to tell you, my darling, I am posted to another operational squadron and have to leave tomorrow. That is why tonight has been so important for us both, as well as so wonderful!'

Jane looked at him, her eyes filling with tears. Pulling herself together, she managed to say, 'Sorry, Tom. I didn't mean to cry. It's just strange that I've had a feeling all evening that tonight might mean our farewell. Everything has been so perfect, and I fully understand how difficult it's been for you, and I love you all the more for it.'

They had reached the wharf and tied up the launch before hugging each other as though there was no tomorrow; finally, they got into Tom's car to return to tell the sad news to Jane's parents. Her father wished the boy all the best of luck and her mother put her arms around him saying, 'Come back safely and God bless you, Tom.'

Mrs Freeman guessed right away what had happened when Jane

appeared the next morning looking tearful and weary. She told her to saddle-up Blackie and take him for a good gallop: 'Perhaps that will help you get things in perspective.' It was at that moment that Jane remembered her lady-boss the previous evening when she was holding a letter and looking very pale. 'Are you sure that *you* feel all right?' she asked.

Mrs Freeman looked away and quietly replied, 'I can only hope and pray, just as you must; I'm afraid John's ship is reported missing, so praying is all I can do.' Jane rushed to her, putting both arms around her dear lady. 'And here am I making such a fuss just because Tom has been posted, and you are all alone here with this awful worry.' She went out to tell Arthur that she was going for a quick ride and would catch up on her jobs later. He asked if she'd heard Mrs Freeman's bad news, saying he was just off to see her.

Jane's spirits brightened as she rode Blackie, and oddly enough, she found herself riding along the river-bank where all the happy memories of the previous evening came flooding back. She finally got things into their right perspective and after a good canter along the tow-path, tied the mare up-to a gate-post; she took off her shoes and socks, rolled up her jodhpurs, and paddled in the cool water, trying her best to put all her worries behind her, and counting her many blessings.

It was with a heavy heart that Jane told her parents Tom's news later that evening, and to her amazement, her mother told her daughter a story she had never mentioned before. Although Jane knew that her mother's marriage to her father was a second one, it had never occurred to her to ask anything about it. In fact, the subject had never been broached. All Jane knew was that when they were much younger, she and her sister had spent many holidays in Lancashire, where her grandfather, the owner of a cotton mill, lived. Her mother proceeded to tell her that during the first world war, she had married the son of a very wealthy mill owner in Rochdale. Almost as soon as they had married, her new husband had joined the army in the 1914/18 war and was sent to the front line. He never returned, having been killed very early on in battle. Her mother, as Jane already knew, had later joined the RFC as a dispatch-rider, and had eventually met Jane's father, who was also in the Royal Flying Corps. They had met at Brooklands, where her mother was based.

After telling Jane this chapter in her life, her mother said, 'I'm not telling you this to upset or to puzzle you, but if it is any consolation at all, it is to show you that in times of war we all have our cross to bear and life has to go on. As I'm sure you know, Tom will be feeling as sad as you – if not more so - and for his sake you must carry on. Keep writing newsy letters to him once you have an address, and keep yourself as busy as possible. Above all, be positive that he will come safely through this.'

This had all been quite a revelation to Jane, and she felt very humble that she had never asked questions of her mother's early life. But she also realised that in wartime there is no certainty; hope and being cheerful are great healers of despair, and right now thousands of mothers, wives and sweethearts would be feeling the same pain. She also remembered Tom's family, especially his wonderful grandmother and brother Nigel, and made up her mind that as soon as possible she would go and see them again, and she would stop feeling sorry for herself right away.

Land girl ch 9

On the Monday of the following week, Deborah arrived to start working with Jane and Susan. She had already worked out her notice on her previous farm and was overjoyed to be leaving it. Back home that evening, Jane decided to attack her letter writing; the first one would naturally have been to Tom had she known where to send it. However, his posting had taken immediate effect and everything was very hush hush. She wrote first of all to his grandmother and parents, mostly telling them about things that were happening on the farm, and only at the end mentioning how very much she was missing Tom.

Her next letter was a rather belated one to Mrs Pick, Michael's mother. She intended writing a cheerful letter, and full of odd things that happened to her on the farm, but the words simply would not come. She really wanted to know about Michael: was he still listed as missing or had Mrs Pick had any further information? But these things needed to be said face to face and she vowed to go and see Mrs Pick on her next day off. Finally, she wrote to Pat giving her all the latest news, asking how she and Bob were doing. By the time she had finished, utter weariness took a hold and there was nothing for it but to go to bed.

Hay-making came and went. Fortunately, the good weather still held, and Jane saw that the corn-fields were also beginning to turn colour. Jane still missed the hens – most of which were now gone. They had been such a large part of her work as a Land girl, and many memories flooded back as she thought back on her first two years with three thousand of them. Now the only ones left were in one house in the paddock just behind the farmhouse. Jane was still kept busy, for there were many new calves arriving - sometimes two in one day - and although work now was very different, there was always plenty to do. She had fun still during off-duty spells, especially now that Deborah had joined them. The May ball in the Officers' Mess was no exception, as it was one of those special occasions. Also there were their games of tennis, and swimming together, and she was able to write about all these things in her letters to Tom. The letters helped the long days go by.

But once again the wretched war news intervened. While she was seeing to the calves one morning Deborah rushed over to tell her that Mrs Freeman seemed distraught. All she could tell her friend was that Mrs Freeman had received a telegram from the Admiralty and she thought Jane ought to go over to the house. It was with great trepidation that she went into the kitchen only to find her lady-boss in floods of tears. This time Mrs Freeman was *not* her usual calm self - she was shaking and weeping uncontrollably. She looked up as Jane went in, and told her sadly, 'Apparently my husband's ship was torpedoed at the time he was reported missing.' She went on to explain that the hope then was that most of the survivors had been picked up, ironically, by the very submarine that had sunk it. It was presumed that all the crew of the Corvette were taken as prisoners of war by the Germans and would be held captive on shore somewhere. This appeared to be so until news reached the Admiralty that Commander Freeman had succumbed to the pneumonia he'd contracted after the sinking, due to the length of time he was left in the water; he'd been in a hospital for many weeks, but had died two days ago.

Her grief was almost unbearable for Jane and she asked, 'Is there anyone I can contact for you? Would you like a cup-of-tea? O*h! what can I do for you*?' she cried in desperation. Both Arthur and Frank arrived and suggested that Jane phone for the doctor to come. Arthur said he would fetch his wife over to be with Mrs Freeman, as he could see that both girls were out of their depth in this situation. They went back across to the farm, arms around one another, both weeping as they carried on with their jobs. Meanwhile, the doctor gave his patient a sleeping draught, promising to look in again later.

Jane suddenly remembered that during one of their talks, Mrs Freeman had mentioned her sister-in-law who lived in Devon. She ran straight back across to the house, determined to find her phone number. This took some doing, but when Jane set out to do something she usually managed it.

Although it took some while to get an answer on the phone, as was always the case during this war, she finally got through and had to give the sad news to the lady who'd answered. A little later when the phone rang it was to say that Mrs Freeman's the sister-in-law, Mrs Tate, was already on her way to the station and would be at their nearest station, Didcot, later that evening around 10:30. Arthur agreed to meet her so that the girls could stay close to Mr Freeman.

As she looked in on Mrs Freeman some hours later Jane found her awake and was able to tell that Mrs Tate was on her way, 'Thank you Jane for all you have done. I *will get over this, and the farm will carry on.* John would not have had it any other way, and with you three girls and our team of loyal workers we will manage.'

Within hours of her arrival, Mrs Tate calmed their devastated lady-boss; she soon settled in, taking charge of running the household. Jane took Susan home with her that first evening, when they eventually felt that they could leave, and Mrs Freeman was given more sedative by her doctor. Neither girl had ever been in this kind of situation before and they felt the need to console each other, and who better to help them than Jane's sympathetic parents. Grieving was going to be hard for Mrs Freeman as there was no body, and therefore no funeral. Such were the conditions during the war, but somehow it left them with a feeling of unfinished business. However, on the farm itself, they all pulled together as never before.

When Tom finally got some leave, Jane's parents said he must stay at their house. Jane felt almost guilty for feeling so happy that her young man was safe and with her once more. He spent every possible moment on the farm, mostly grooming and riding the two hunters, or helping out with whatever task was needed. After a few days, Tom told Jane and her parents that he must go down to see his own family; apparently his grandmother was getting more and more frail, and of course, they all wanted to see him. He told them that Jane would not be going this time since she felt she couldn't leave her lady-boss, which they quite understood.

Mrs Freeman mentioned to Jane that maybe she ought to think about selling the two hunters, although she was reluctant to do this, and wondered if Tom knew anybody who might be able to spare the time to ride them? When he telephoned Jane that evening, she inquired about his grandmother and also asked him about the hunters. He told her that as soon as he returned he would try to find someone from the aerodrome to ride the horses. Tom told her that he'd often been envied when his pals knew he had horses he could ride; therefore, he felt sure one or other of them would welcome this opportunity.

On his return from Dorset, Tom kept his promise and did ask friends on the airfield; in no time, Mrs Freeman had riders for the two horses. She was so pleased that she hadn't to part with them, at least for the foreseeable future. Meantime, the pilot and his Land girl spent every possible moment with each other, and both Benny and Deborah made sure of this, taking turns to cover Jane's work. Inevitably, the last night of Tom's leave came and their evening started almost where it had begun, together in the Castle pub. Many of Tom's former RAF buddies were there and, as the saying goes, 'a good time was had by all' - that is, except Jane, who simply dreaded saying goodbye this time. Nigel appeared later in the evening and promised Jane that he would take Tom to the station the next morning, knowing that he wouldn't want a public farewell; both Jane and Tom were grateful to him for this offer.

After their goodbyes, Jane finally got to grips with her emotions as she cycled to the farm early the following morning. As she recalled all the wonderful memories of their times together, she remembered that they were just two of the millions who had to say goodbye to their loved ones.

Harvest was in full flow once again and she gritted her teeth and worked as hard as any of the men during those next few weeks.

Land girl ch 10

As Mr Freeman's sister had now taken charge of running the house and looking after Jane's grieving boss, things began to change a little. It had been a difficult time since there had been no funeral and therefore no closure. Everyone at the farm still had the feeling of 'unfinished business.' However, there was work to be done, and a local farmer, and great friend, offered agricultural advice as and when it was necessary; thus they all pulled together in order to continue the smooth running of the farm.

One evening, Nigel telephoned her at home asking if she would go with him to the local hop which Tom had told him about. She hesitated before giving an answer; understanding her hesitation, Nigel told her that Tom had especially asked him to do this, and so finally she agreed. Fortunately, both Deborah and Susan were there, and Deborah obviously made quite a hit with Nigel, which left Jane free to dance with her other friends. Nevertheless, he was there to take her home and behaved perfectly - much better than at their previous meeting in Dorset.

Nigel continued to be a good friend to Jane, and whenever he could he invited her to dances in the mess, usually inviting Deborah and Susan too. But one evening, Jane's friend told her that although she had shown Nigel how very much she liked him, in fact cared for him, he remained aloof. 'Maybe it's because, like Tom, he is on operational flying and wants to keep his life uncomplicated. Have you considered that?' 'No, but I'd prefer him to be a little more romantic,' said Deborah. Jane advised her to be patient and not try to rush things, reminding her what had only recently happened to Mrs Freeman.

Several evenings later while at home, Jane had a call from Tom; pleased as she was to hear from him, she was a little alarmed when he asked, 'Do you think you could possibly get any time off to go down to Dorset to see my parents? They are getting very anxious about grandma.' Naturally, Jane agreed to do this and told him that if it *was* possible she would go as soon as she could be spared. They chatted for a while and before Tom rang off she asked, 'Do you know that your brother is on the nearby aerodrome again?' Tom told her that he did know as they had been in touch and that he'd asked Nigel to look after her and make sure that she didn't get too lonely. This made her feel a whole lot better, and they talked for a few more minutes before the operator said their time was up and goodbyes had to be said.

The very next morning, Jane approached Arthur about asking their lady-boss for a few days' leave. He did so, and Mrs Freeman said she was pleased to give her some time off as she'd been under quite a lot of stress recently, one way and another. That very evening, Jane rang through to the Gregory household and, much to their delight, arranged to go down in two days' time.

The following morning, she met Deborah, who seemed miserable. Jane asked what the trouble was, and Deb told her that her date with Nigel had been cancelled as he'd gone away for a few days. Jane consoled her by telling her about her own few days' leave, and said, 'You can take over as many of my jobs as you like, and they will keep you so busy you won't have time to brood over Nigel!'

Her father drove her to the station at Didcot, which was not too far and would not use too much of his precious petrol. When she got into the carriage, Jane found it extremely hot and stuffy, and she was glad to be out of uniform and in a light summery dress. To open a window meant getting covered in black smuts from the steam engine - she remembered this from her trip up to London and vowed not to do that again! A few soldiers and two WAAFS were also in the carriage but they all looked tired and strained which made her feel that no attempt at conversation was necessary, so she settled back and quietly dozed off. Waking up suddenly she heard, 'Poole. Next stop Bournemouth'. With a start, she gathered-up her belongings, opened the carriage door and jumped out onto the platform almost right into the arms of the young man who'd come to meet her.

'Steady on there,' a familiar voice cried as she almost knocked over the fair-haired young RAF officer. Looking up, she saw that it was Nigel, who'd come to meet her train. 'Yes it's me again!' he told her, grinning at her look of amazement. 'You look as brown as a berry with your hair even more blonded in the front than when we met last. Now, let's go and get a cup of tea somewhere before I drive you home.'

Over tea, she told Nigel of Mr Freeman's death and how it had affected everyone on the farm. 'I expect Deborah has told you all this already'. 'Well, actually, I've not seen quite so much of her lately. Things are hotting up yet again on the airfield and there's been little free time, but also your friend seems to want to get far too serious,' he explained to Jane.

After finishing their tea, they climbed into Nigel's old car and made their way to his parents' home. As they drove along, Jane noticed how very pretty scenery was, and this, along with the lack of aircraft noise, helped her to relax. She noticed another ring on Nigel's tunic-sleeve, denoting that he was now a Wing Commander. She congratulated him and he said, 'Yes, accelerated promotion! I suppose it's compensation, if you can call it that. I've been posted over-seas, in fact, to North Africa. That's why I'm here on leave at the moment. The other reason of course, is to see my grandmother before I go - she's getting very frail, as mother may well have told you.' Jane told him that was the reason she was here and that Tom had asked her to come, as he wasn't able to get leave at present. She also thought to herself, I will have a pretty wretched Deborah on my hands when I get back to the farm, for sure.

Turning down the narrow lane leading to the Gregory's house, they were brought to a standstill by a flock of sheep blocking their way, totally unattended. They decided to get them into the nearest empty field if possible, and as they did so, Nigel laughed saying, 'You are in your element, whereas I'm completely useless, so you'll have to tell me what I must do.' 'Open the gate of the first field we come to and if there is grass in it they will happily go in,' she told him. Having managed to accomplish this, which left both of them hot and dusty, Nigel remarked, 'I hadn't expected to be joining the land army quite this soon!' 'We'd better press on and phone from your place to see which farmer owns them, or maybe your parents will know,' Jane told him.

She ran into the house as soon as Nigel stopped the car and finding nobody about, went through to the garden. There she found Mr & Mrs Gregory sitting in deck-chairs in their pretty garden. After the welcoming handshakes and hugs, Jane went to freshen up before supper, leaving Nigel to deal with the sheep and their owners. Mrs Gregory told Jane how pleased they were that she had got a few days' leave and that grandma would perk-up no end at seeing her once more. 'She often asks about you,' said Mrs Gregory, 'what with the war and the worry about its toll. Even in this seemingly peaceful part of the country, it's a constant concern - together with the fact that she can no longer cope with her garden, nor find anyone to help because all the local lads have been conscripted.' Jane asked if it would be too late for her to go along to grandma's cottage after they'd had supper, saying that she could only stay a few days and didn't want to waste any time. 'Nigel will come along with you I'm sure, and you can see for yourself what help you can give. I'm sure he will be pleased to give you a hand.' Jane noticed the twinkle in Mrs Gregory's eye, as she spoke loudly enough for her son to hear. They left after Jane had helped to clear and wash up the supper dishes. Nigel told his parents that they might pop into the local after they'd been to see his gran.

Jane was quite upset when she saw just how much Mrs Gregory, senior, had deteriorated since her last visit. Now, she could barely get out of her chair, needed two sticks to help her walk, and seemed to ramble quite a bit talking about things as they used to be. But between them they managed to find out what exactly they could do in the garden for her. Conversation about the garden did seem to brighten her up, and it was obviously much on her mind that it needed attention; they made plans to arrive the following morning to tackle at least the part that she could see from her chair.

Nigel said he thought they both needed a drink and Jane agreed to visit the local before going back to his parents', as she was feeling pretty thirsty. She was welcomed once more by everyone she had met on her previous visit with Tom. Nigel explained that he was looking after his brother's girl, telling them that he was on active duty at present, and that they'd come to see his gran. Most of them knew old Mrs Gregory and asked after her. They had obviously heard that her health was failing, as news like that travelled fast in a small village.

Jane enjoyed talking to the men as well as their wives or sweethearts who were in the pub. She was asked all the usual questions about being in the land-army, and of course how Tom was and what he was doing. Some questions she could and did answer, but about Tom and his flying she said very little. After a while Jane began to feel weary; she had been up since the crack-of-dawn, after all, and as Nigel was happily playing darts she signalled that she was leaving, telling him to stay as she was happy to go on her own.

Mrs Gregory and her husband had already retired but as Nigel's mother had not heard his car she came downstairs to ask if everything was all right. Jane explained that he was enjoying the company of his friends but that she had got rather weary. Mrs Gregory heated some milk and asked how her mother had seemed to her. 'Well, she does need some help, and I am going to make an early start on her garden in the morning,' Jane told her, 'and I hope Nigel will come along so that we can get most of it done.' Then, saying 'goodnight', a weary Jane finally got to her bed.

There was no sign of Nigel the following morning and so Jane went off on her own. She found Mrs Gregory senior. still in bed, although her daily help had been in to take her breakfast up and wash her. Gran was pleased to see Jane, although she got the feeling that the old lady had forgotten that she'd even been there the day before, let alone had Nigel with her. After a brief chat about the garden, Jane left her dozing and went downstairs to start work. Suddenly, a voice called 'wait for me,' and it was Nigel!

He looked a bit sheepish, and began to apologise for his lateness. It was apparent that he was still slightly hung-over, but to give him his due, he began work on the lawns with gusto! By lunchtime they had the whole garden looking almost like it used to be, and when Jane saw that Mrs Gregory was now downstairs, she helped her outside so that she could see what they had accomplished. Her old eyes said everything! There was no need for any words, and both Jane and Nigel felt that was reward enough.

The doorbell rang just then and Jane found that it was a Meals-On- Wheels lady coming with gran's lunch. They chatted a while as Nigel helped the old lady into her chair. Once she was comfortably settled with her lunch they left, telling her that they would call in before leaving in the morning. 'Make sure that you bring young Tom with you then,' she told them, and naturally this brought tears to Jane's eyes, not knowing when that would be possible again. Noticing this, but not appearing to notice, Nigel took Jane's arm as they walked back to his parents' home. By the time they'd reached it, she was her old self again, and mumbled her thanks to Nigel.

Land girl Ch 11

The following morning when Jane came down for breakfast there was no Nigel, and when Mrs Gregory returned from the shop with the newspaper, she told Jane that Nigel had had an urgent recall to his unit and had left the house very early.' He asked me to thank you for insisting that he helped with his gran's garden, and said to tell you that you are quite a bully! He sent you his love, saying he'd see you around sometime!' Jane thought quite seriously about this message later that day, when she was out for a walk on her own. Her host and hostess were lunching with friends and Jane had not wanted to intrude, also she wanted to see more of the Dorset countryside. Walking along, she remembered Nigel's message and smiled to herself; he really was quite a character, but a nice person all the same.

She called in at a small but inviting-looking pub, very quiet; she asked if they did bar-snacks, the answer was yes - soup with home-made bread. Jane said this would be fine and she would have a half of bitter shandy to go with it. The landlady seemed to want to chatter, whereas Jane simply wanted to sit in peace and enjoy the view, which was of the sea with the rocks of Old Harry jutting out in the distance. Also she could see the moorland of the Purbecks where she'd just walked; all in all, very peaceful and lovely, without the sound of aircraft or gunfire.

As she didn't want to appear unfriendly, Jane did explain to the landlady about her job in the Land Army and the operational airfield nearby. When Jane enthused about this beautiful part of England, the landlady agreed that she and her husband were lucky to be living in Dorset. She told Jane about her life in London, the rushing in and out of air-raid shelters, and the friends she'd lost already in this war. Later on, two other people came along wanting lunch and so Jane was left in peace. She went back inside to return her plates and glass and this time it was the landlord who said, 'Well at last we've had a Land Army girl in our pub! You are the very first and I hope we'll see you again, and jolly good luck to you.'

Jane called in to see grandma on her way back, and this time found the old lady sitting in her garden with her cat on her knee. She greeted Jane as though she'd not seen her for weeks saying, 'I had a nice young man and girl come in and tidy-up my garden, doesn't it look nice?' Smiling, Jane agreed. She realised just how the dear lady's mind was deteriorating; but then she chatted normally for a while before she slowly dozed off. Jane slipped quietly away wondering if she would still be around when her precious grandsons had finished their operational tours; she offered up a silent prayer that she would.

All too soon, it was time for Jane to return to her own duties and as Tom's mother drove her to the station she voiced her concern over the old lady. Mrs Gregory, ever practical, said, 'She has had a wonderful life and, as you have seen, she is well looked after, both by ourselves and her many friends. But I must say it's been wonderful the way you have brightened these past few days for her, so all our thanks go to you, and we pray that Tom will come safely through for you as well for us.'

On the journey back, Jane was in the company of soldiers returning from leave. They talked away to her; some with sadness at having left wives and sweethearts, others with expectation as to their next movements, yet all knowing that a second front was very much 'on the cards' in the near future.

Thinking about, this Jane guessed this was why she'd heard so little from Tom. There was so much to be done before the final assault could come about; she wondered too if maybe this was why Nigel had been recalled early. The journey back to Didcot seemed quite fast, what with all the banter and the chatter, especially once she had admitted to being a Land girl!

Her father was at the station to meet her train, and as always, gave her a big hug; she thought he looked very tired and told him so. He said that he had been on 'fire-watching duty' the previous night. Jane next asked if there was anything bothering him, other than the shortage of building materials and even the shortage of the need for his services as a builder. He merely mumbled something about the 'whole bloody war.'

Later, talking to her mother, she gathered that her sister Kathleen was getting rather serious about the American master-sergeant she was seeing, and talks of an engagement were being bandied about. Although both Jane's parents liked 'Dusty' they had not envisaged things getting quite that serious so soon. 'But mother, Tom and I have also discussed becoming engaged; there is no time to hang around with this wretched war going on and on,' her daughter informed her. 'Yes! We realise how fond you two are of one another, but you won't be leaving us to live in America once it's all over, as Kathleen will.'

This, then, was why her father was not his usual self Jane decided; but her sister *was* twenty-three years old and this kind of thing was happening everywhere, all the time. Her parents would simply have to accept the situation.

Back at the farm, Jane noticed that Frank had just finished

cutting one of the larger wheat-fields, and seeing her, he walked over saying he hoped she'd enjoyed her break: 'There's going to be some 'ard work ahead for you and them other two girls.' 'I can see that, but I'm pleased I went to Dorset, for Tom's sake. It wasn't exactly enjoyable this time - his grandma is definitely not as well as the last time Tom and I were there. How have things been here?' she asked him. 'The normal work on a farm has to go on, and now that the initial shock is over the missus seems to have accepted the situation very well. She comes across every morning to talk to us about the every-day running of things and everyone seems to be pulling together, but she'll no doubt tell you herself when you goes to the 'ouse. I'll tell you one thing, that 'oss 'as missed you, so've the dogs. You'll find there are one or two more young calves now, and we've put your 'Monty-what-sis-name' out in the paddock.' 'Thanks for all the news, Frank. A lot seems to have happened in just a few days.' 'Mr Smythe, you know, the farmer along the road, 'as been sorting a few things out for 'er, and we all likes and respects 'im as you know. It seems Mrs Freeman intends to keep the farm and we're all glad about that.'

As Jane rode off she said, 'See you tomorrow then Frank. I'm just so pleased that all our jobs seem to be safe. My fears that the farm might have to be sold were a bit premature, thank goodness.' As she reached the farmhouse, Deborah came running out to tell her that Tom was on the 'phone. Jane handed Blackie over to her and dashed into the house. 'Jane darling, I rang home and mother said you'd left. How are things? How is Mrs Freeman, and how are you now?' 'Hang on a minute Tom, it's wonderful to hear your voice, I've missed it so much and I've missed you most of all. Things were good at your parents, and grandma sent her love, and here, Mrs Freeman is coping well and is keeping the farm - which is good news for everyone. As for me, I feel much better for my break, but can't wait to see you again, so do take great care, for all our sakes, especially your grandma. And incidentally, I'm living here now. Susan and I share a room, and we help get the meals for us all. Mrs Freeman prefers it this way, and my parents are happy about it, thank goodness.' They chatted to one another for a few more minutes until Jane heard the operator telling Tom his time was up. After the phone talk, Jane was very quiet, and went off back to her work, without another word. Fortunately the others understood, yet all were a bit anxious about her.

She was her usual bright self again the next morning as she set about her normal jobs; but she still had a feeling of unease, nonetheless. When Deborah met up with her, she chatted away, telling Jane she was enjoying her many visits to the village 'hops,' and had made quite a number of friends. She was also a good listener, and Jane told her all about Tom's family and her few days staying with them; she also confided in her about her own continual unease about her loved-one and his flying.

'Mrs Freeman seems to have got over the worst,' Deborah observed. 'We are fortunate that she's decided to carry on with the farm.' 'I wonder if it was left in her name?' Jane mused, 'Don't suppose Mr Freeman could possibly have done otherwise since she's been running it all the time he's been away.' Deborah then informed her friend that Arthur had told her that they would be expanding the herd, so there would always be plenty for all of them to do.

A few days later, it was all hands on deck in the harvest field, and Jane wondered yet again how she ever thought there wouldn't be sufficient work for them; by the end of the second day they were almost too exhausted to even laugh, let alone think of going out in the evening. Bath and bed was all they could consider after each hard day's work.

Meanwhile, Mrs Freeman was not looking at all well when they left the following morning. Jane stayed behind and eventually Mrs Freeman told her that the doctor had said she must see a specialist about the continual back and stomach pains she was getting, and that it was now all in hand.

Some weeks later, there was the non-stop sound of engines, of aeroplanes flying in and out. There was also a complete disappearance of any RAF personnel in or around the village. Everyone was aware that London and other big cities had been, and still were being, constantly bombed night and day by the Luftwaffe. Yet morale continued to be good, mainly due to the Prime Minister, Winston Churchill.

His words in 1940 were never to be forgotten, 'We shall fight on the beaches, we shall fight on the landing-grounds, we shall fight in the fields and in the streets, we shall fight in the hills. We shall *never surrender.*' Words such as these kept the morale high as he continually praised the ordinary people for their work and their courage.

The bombing of German cities went on day after day, night after night; losses were high on both sides. But it was clear that the RAF was now well supplied with planes and with pilots to fly them. More and more women were called to take part in the industrial effort; officials reckoned it would take three women to do the work of two men, but the women proved them wrong.

The Land girls continued with their everyday work, come what may, and some were actually given a pay rise, though not so in Oxfordshire. That reward was to come two years later. Meanwhile, many had to put up with having to work alongside either German or Italian prisoners of war. In fact, Jane and Deborah were to find that they, too, had Italians coming to their farm to help with the threshing later on that year.

With a larger milking herd there was more work to be done both in the dairy and the cowshed, but all three were able to help now that the harvest was safely gathered in once more. Jane set to in the garden at the farmhouse: flower-beds went, and in their place she planted more and more vegetables for use in the house - anything to help with the meagre rations. All over the country people were asked to 'Dig for victory,' and they did.

She still found time to ride Blackie and exercise the dogs at the same time; also, lately she had accompanied Mrs Freeman when she went shopping in the tub-cart, in order to do the queuing to save her the tiring and painful periods of standing. All three girls knew by now that something was very wrong physically with their boss, and that she was shortly having something done about it.

The problem solved itself finally, for one night, Mrs Freeman became really ill. This time, she was in excruciating pain. Susan and Deborah promptly sent for both the doctor and the ambulance. It was late evening by the time they arrived at the farm; Jane said that she would go in the ambulance with her boss, but this time Deborah insisted on going, with the promise to ring the farm as soon as she knew what was happening.

Land girl ch 12

There was much talk and press comment about a 'Second Front', and it seemed that most parts of the British Isles were 'home' to the armed forces as the Navy, Army and Air Forces continued to grow in strength. Jane naturally feared for both Nigel and Tom, and she began to feel the same tension that millions of others were enduring for their loved ones' safety.

Most of the next day, Jane worked on her vegetable plot near to the house where she could hear the telephone if it rang; everything was growing well - and so it should, Jane thought, with all the farmyard manure I've given it. Trying hard to distract herself from the immediate worry about Mrs Freeman and the black cloud of the war, she picked plenty of runner beans and the last of the peas. This gave her a great deal of satisfaction as she plunged her hands into the warm, growing vegetables. She thought, too, 'Dad would be proud of me'- it was he who had taught her all she knew about gardening from an early age. She cycled home that evening, and was able to pour out all her worries about the war to her parents – and her worries about Mrs Freeman. Jane was also able to tell her father that all he'd taught her about gardening was coming to fruition, and that picking the 'harvest' was both calming and exciting.

As always, it had been the right decision to go and see her parents. She left later in the evening for her cycle back to the farm, feeling *so* much less stressed; her parents understood just how fond their daughter was of not only her boss, but of the farm itself and everyone there. Late that night, Deborah rang from the hospital to say that the specialist had been to see Mrs Freeman, that he'd seen the test results and hoped to be doing an operation within the next two days. Then she told them she was about to catch the last bus back from Oxford and would fill them in with more details when she arrived. Jane and Susan stayed up until they heard a taxi come, hoping it would be Deborah, and were relieved when she bounded into the house. Deborah reiterated that Mrs Freeman was now waiting for surgery to relieve the pain in her back and legs. For now, they were all on hold.

The following evening Jane rang through to Tom's parents, and although they were pleased to hear from her, Jane could sense the anxiety in Mrs Gregory's voice. She told her that Nigel had at last written to tell them to stop worrying about him! They were all kept pretty busy on his squadron and there was little that he could tell them because of the sensitive nature of their activities. Jane then asked about grandma, and was told, 'She seems to be giving up, and we have got her here with us now, so that we can look after her all the time. But thank you for ringing - we think of you often with your own worry about Tom.' Jane sent her love to all, and gave Mrs Gregory the news of Mrs Freeman's trouble, and her own talk with Tom. She also said she hoped to be able to visit them as soon as the crisis with Mrs Freeman was over and she was back home again.

The two girls went into the village the following evening, and found it almost bereft of males. Just a few Land girls from nearby farms and a couple of ATS girls who were on leave were out and about. The jolly WVS ladies told them that rations were getting tighter than ever, so it was just as well that not too many hungry airmen were about. Jane and Susan went along to the local pub before going home, and there, too, it was quiet - apart from the droning of bombers flying overhead. It seemed almost surreal, and yet it was palpably real.

Jane and Susan had cycled down to the village that evening. On their way back, Susan hit something in the road, for in the blackout it was difficult enough to see even the side of the road, let alone a huge stone lying there. She was thrown over her bike handlebars and cracked her face hard on the road surface. Jane dropped her own bike and tried to help her up; Susan was quite shocked, and staggered to her feet holding her face with both hands. With her cycle light, such as it was, Jane could see that she was bleeding profusely from her nose, so she sat Susan down on the grass verge and used what handkerchiefs they had to stem the bleeding. But it wouldn't stop; fortunately they were quite near to Frank's cottage and she told her friend to stay put while she went for help. Both Frank and his wife Amy ran out straight away, and they managed to get Susan inside. When they had had a good look at the damage, Amy got a bowl of warm water for Jane to bathe and clean Susan's face. Next, they gently put her down flat on the floor to try to stop the bleeding. Amy went to make a cup of tea for the girls while Frank grinned at Susan saying, 'You'll have a whopper there by morning, lass!' It was a good hour later before Susan felt able to walk home with Jane holding on to her, while Frank pushed their bicycles.

Once back at the farm, Jane bathed Susan's face again and could see that the deep graze on her forehead was already beginning to swell. 'My nose and head hurt a lot,' her friend told her. Looking closely at her, Jane said, 'We'd better get you to a doctor in the morning, just to make sure nothing is broken.' Susan agreed, but felt for now that it was 'time for bed for us both I think - but thanks for all your help.' Jane helped her friend up the stairs, but, quiet as they were, Deborah either heard or sensed something and was standing on the landing asking what was wrong. As soon as she saw Susan's face and head she cried anxiously, 'What on earth has happened?' All three sat on her bed as Jane told her the story, 'For one terrible moment I thought she had been hit by a bomb.'

The following morning, Jane rang the surgery and made an appointment to take Susan along, but before she went she gave Deborah and Arthur a hand with the cows and got Benny to do some of her feeding. The doctor was not too happy about Susan and wanted some x-rays done. This meant a phone call to the cottage hospital in nearby Wallingford to arrange for this, and then a call to the farm letting them know why they'd not be back before afternoon. The result came the following day when the doctor visited Susan. Thankfully, nothing was broken but there was severe bruising, and he insisted that Susan had the rest of the week off work. It was Arthur who said that as soon as she felt able she should have some leave and go home for a good rest. Both Deborah and Jane were pleased he'd suggested this for the accident had certainly shaken Susan up, and with her bruised and swollen nose, the slightest jolt would cause her agony. Three days later, Jane drove her friend to the station to catch a train home; even then, every bump in the road caused the poor girl to wince.

Land girl ch 13

That night Jane could not settle. So many things were on her mind, the main one being Susan. Also, the complete and utter silence from Tom once again was wearing on her. This she found so hard to cope with. In the end she went downstairs and made herself a cup of tea; it was only 3.00am, but she could hear heavy bombers droning across the sky, followed by planes taking off from the nearby airfield. Daylight was just about to break when an enormous thud rocked the house. 'What on earth was that?' Deborah's sleepy voice called. 'I think the airfield's been hit - either that or a plane has crashed,' Jane answered. 'I'll take a look around outside, but you stay here.' She walked around outside the house and was crossing the yard to the farm buildings when Arthur appeared, dressed as she was, with a coat over his pyjamas. 'The aerodrome seems to have caught one,' he told her. 'You can see fires from our bedroom window. Nothing seems to be hit here, thank goodness, but I'll bet it's scared some of the animals. We best get dressed, then we'll take a proper look at them.'

When they had both dressed and met up again, they saw that the horses were careering about the field, ears and tails up! The cows too, were rushing around - tails high in the air, a sure sign that they were scared. The three dogs were barking and whining to be let out and to be pacified. The cart-horses, apart from Prince the younger one, seemed only puzzled by the bang. However, Prince's coat looked to be in a bit of a lather so they decided to get him into his stable to calm him down. Jane went to look at Montgomery who was rushing madly around his enclosure; she slowly approached him, talking gently all the time, until at last he calmed down, allowing her to fondle him.

He soon became his old self and began nudging her, which he always did when he was feeling playful. She pulled some nice juicy-looking grass and gave it to him, leaving him a reassured and contented animal.

When all the animals seemed settled, Jane and Arthur went in to the kitchen, both in need of the cup of tea, which Deborah had thoughtfully brewed in readiness for them. The rest of the day passed uneventfully. Much later, they heard that there had, indeed, been a bomb on the airfield and that four planes had been wrecked. Also, one of the hangers was completely destroyed, but fortunately nobody was killed or even hurt.

.Just as she had finished her work and was enjoying her cup of tea, the telephone rang. Picking it up she heard Tom's voice: 'Jane, my darling, you must have wondered where I'd got to!

I've longed to hear your voice for *so many weeks*! And now at last here you are on the other end of the phone.' 'Dearest Tom, I've been so worried not hearing or getting a letter. Are you all right?' she asked, in a shaky voice. 'It's a long story, but yes I'm okay now - just been out of action for a while. But I can fill you in later - I'm on a 48-hour pass, so can I come to the farm, say about midday tomorrow, if that's all right?' 'Of course it's all right! I've so much to tell you. Will you be in your car, or do you want us to meet somewhere else?' 'I'll get a taxi, so don't worry; and by the way, I really love you very much and hope and pray you feel the same.'

Jane almost floated all the way to the hospital that evening as she drove down to see Mrs Freeman, and, when she had parked the car, she found she could hardly remember driving the 14 miles to Oxford. Tom would be here tomorrow! She felt happier than she had in months, and what months they'd been: one thing after another! She burst into Mrs Freeman's room and found her, thankfully, looking less strained, and obviously not in so much pain. She was so pleased at the sight of Jane's smiling face: 'I'd guess you've heard from Tom! I can't think of any other reason that you would look so happy,' she said, smiling back at Jane. 'Yes! But first, how are you? Is everything progressing satisfactorily?' Mrs Freeman smiled, 'Things are moving slowly but in the right direction. *Now, will you tell me about Tom?*'

'First of all, he's all right. I don't know any details yet, but he's coming over tomorrow, and has two days' leave - so would it be all right if he stays at the farm for the night?' 'Of course it will be all right! You don't need to ask,' was her reply. 'Thank goodness you will be seeing him - that's why there's a big smile back on your face! Now, tell me all the other news.' After that Jane told her, first about the bombing of the aerodrome, then of Susan's unfortunate accident. Mrs Freeman's immediate thought was for Susan, and once she'd heard all the details, insisted that her Land girl go home on leave. 'She has already gone. The doctor more or less gave the order, and as we didn't want to worry you, we sent her off! We hope you don't mind,' Jane told her boss.

Later, as she was driving back, she suddenly began to feel extremely tired. Pulling herself together, she knew that she must concentrate on the road - Tom was coming tomorrow, and life felt good again. Having put the car away, she looked in on Deborah and for once was pleased to find her fast asleep. She herself could barely keep her eyes open and fell on to the bed without even taking her clothes off.

She could hardly contain herself the following morning. Arthur was soon informed about Tom, as were all the others. Frank told Jane he would cover the afternoon work for her so that she could be free to spend time with Tom; meanwhile, she used the rest of the morning to give Montgomery a good grooming, followed by a lesson in being led with a halter on. After lunch, she went down the lane hoping to meet Tom before he reached the house. She saw a taxi slowing down just as it reached her, and barely recognised Tom as he gingerly stepped out. His face was red all down one side and half the hair was missing from that side of his head; then, as he put out a hand to her, she saw that it too had been injured. 'Jane darling, I've waited so long to give you a big hug and now I'm hardly able. Come here and let me look at you.' After the first shock of seeing him like this, she hugged him, kissing the uninjured side of his face, 'Oh Tom, whatever has happened to you?'

'Can we go into the house while I sit down to tell you about it? It'll be good to see your lady-boss again.' 'Yes, of course we'll go in, but I have to tell you that Mrs Freeman is not here. She's in hospital, and about to have quite a major operation. I'm still not sure what exactly the trouble is but I know that she's been in considerable pain lately.' 'Gosh, that poor lady has had one thing after another. She certainly is a plucky one,' Tom said, 'Are there any more problems you have to tell me about?' 'Well, yes, there is one. Susan and I were cycling home from the village the other evening in the dark when she hit a fairly big stone lying in the road, it sent her flying over the handlebars; she has a very battered and bruised face, and has just gone home for some leave and to recuperate.' As Tom looked aghast, Jane pushed him to tell his story: 'Now I want to know what happened to you,?' Sitting down with his arms around his girl. Tom began to tell her

106

about his own accident. 'I'd been on a sortie and caught some flak on my way back when I was almost home. The fuel tank got hit, and just as the flames began enveloping me I managed to get out. Fortunately, I made it safely and got picked up pretty smartly by one of our own transport trucks which took me to the nearest RAF hospital. Anyway I am alive, the burns are healing well and if I'd not yanked off my flying helmet I'd not have lost so much of my hair.'

Jane asked sharply, 'How soon will you be back flying again?' Tom told her that he had to report to the burns-unit when his 48-hour pass was over. Then he hoped to have some leave and visit his parents, and then 'who knows?' Tom looked pretty exhausted with all this talking, and after drinking the tea Jane made for them, she showed him up to the room she'd got ready for him. After some gentle canoodling she left him to rest; all the while she could not help thinking about how he might well have burned to death, and she said a silent prayer of thanks for his escape.

As she helped Arthur with the milking later, he noticed her very white face under its usual suntan, and heard the story of Tom's lucky escape. He wanted to console her but thought it better not to let her dwell on 'what might have been', asking instead if she felt up to dealing with the calves. Her immediate reaction was 'of course, it's my job and they are hungry' and off she went to feed the four new babies. The few chickens in the paddock were her next stop, and she was extra pleased to find some two dozen lovely brown eggs; these she would give to Tom to take along to his parents the following day. Packing them carefully in a box, she went quietly upstairs.

He had just woken up, having slept solidly since Jane had gone back to work, and he looked much better for the rest. She wanted to know if his burns were still hurting much: 'Just a bit, though it's having this almost useless hand that gets to me! Other than that I'm pretty well fit again, but what about you? What with Mr Freeman's death, then his wife with all her leg trouble and on top of that Susan's smashed face, and now me, how on earth have you coped?' Jane's reply was typical of her acceptance of things:'It's been all go, I must say, but because I've been so worried about you, not a letter or a phone call in all these weeks, I've been glad to be occupied. Why didn't you write or phone, Tom?' 'It's the usual excuse I'm afraid - we have been flying flat-out, getting extremely tired, losing chaps almost daily; it's only having someone like you to think about and to come back to that has kept me going. I'm so very sorry darling, it's the war and the price we're all having to pay.' He took a deep breath and continued: 'When it's all over, we will be together, I promise you. Meanwhile, will you wear the ring grandma gave you until such time that I can buy an official one for you? In other words, Jane, will you marry me once this war is over?' This came as a complete surprise. Certainly, they had discussed their future, but this seemed too much like tempting fate; all the same her reply was immediate, 'Yes. Yes, of course I will, it's all I'll ever want, just to have you back safe and sound, and be with you for always.'

She would have loved to have gone home with Tom, but with her boss still in hospital, and Susan being hurt and now on leave, it was simply not possible. Arthur told Tom when they met the following morning that he would gladly have given Jane time off to be with him but unfortunately he just wasn't able to in the circumstances. He wished them both every happiness when he heard that they had become engaged, and promised Tom that they would have a celebration on his next visit. By the afternoon all the men had been to offer their congratulations. Arthur's wife rose to the occasion and opened a bottle to toast them both, for her husband had quickly put her in the picture.

After supper, during which Jane had cut Tom's food up for him, once she'd seen the difficulty he was having with this simple task, she became concerned about the reality of his situation. 'Does anyone help you with things like this on the station?' she asked. 'So far I've only been in the hospital, where everyone helps one another. Mother is sure to make a fuss when I get home, but I'll just have to hope for the best when I return to work. It's a pity I can't take you with me,' Tom responded, with a smile..

On the drive to the hospital to see Mrs Freeman the two love-birds talked about their future together once the war was over. Jane asked Tom what he might want to do and his immediate reply was that he wanted to fly with one of the air-lines if possible. This was not what his newly acquired fiancée had hoped to hear. However, she knew that prior to war being declared, he'd been at university, therefore had no special job to return to. They sat together on a wooden seat recently donated to the hospital by a grateful patient; it was under a beautiful copper beech tree, and they were very content to just be with each other. After a while, they went in and found that Mrs Freeman was really positive about her operation and its outcome, and her day was brightened all the more because of their visit. Jane told her of their engagement, which really made her happy, and she hugged them as best she could, despite the pain she was in. 'When I get home and you are on leave again Tom, we will have a real celebration,' she told them.

Tom offered-up a silent little prayer, hoping that they would be able to fulfil her wish, yet knowing there were many air-battles yet to be won before the Germans were defeated. Tom remembered then to offer his somewhat belated condolences on her husband's death, asking her if she was going to carry on with the farm. Her reply was firm, as he'd expected from this plucky lady. ' John would have wanted me to, and it's what I want. I'm so lucky now with three hard-working and conscientious girls, not to mention the loyal men on the farm.'

They stayed until the ward sister rang the bell, which meant the end of visiting; both of them gave the patient a gentle hug as they left, with Tom wishing her a speedy recovery.

Land girl ch14

When they eventually got back to the farm, having stopped for a drink in their local, Jane told Tom, 'Call me if you need any help at all,' for she could see that he was feeling whacked and ready for his bed. She laughed when he said, 'You bet I will. I've been used to having a nurse around me for most of the night!'

But before he went, Tom grabbed her hand with his own good one, 'Come here, you wonderful Land girl you, and give me some big kisses before you leave me to go to your bed.' 'Oh, Tom, you've no idea how happy I feel now that I know you are safe and probably won't be flying again for a while. It's been a nightmare not knowing anything. I do wish I could come home with you tomorrow - please give them all my love and especially your gran.' They parted reluctantly, as do all those in love, but they were very happy and thankful that they'd had these precious 48 hours together.

The next morning, Tom was up even before Jane or Deborah and he told them he'd had the best night's sleep in a long time, and who wouldn't with two lovely nurses watching over him. There were hugs all round and tears too as Jane said goodbye to Tom, but at least she knew he would be phoning her and safe, while still on leave.

After Arthur and Deborah had finished the milking and were having breakfast, Jane remembered to phone her own parents with the good news that she'd had Tom with her for his 48-hour pass and that she would go after work to tell them all her news.

It was now only a few days before the agricultural show where

Jane was taking Montgomery. Arthur was taking one of their finest Ayrshire in-calf heifers. There was thus plenty of work to keep her from missing Tom too much: she had to organise a cowman from a local farm to take over Arthur's job with the cows, and show Deborah all her own work, for the two days they'd be away. Benny was also to help with some of her outside jobs and Dobbin was to see to Blackie. It was still beautiful summer weather even now in mid-September; and with everyone helping, both animals were in readiness for the show and looking absolutely top-class. All the shampooing, scrubbing and curry-combing had paid off and both looked in fine form. Tom had phoned Jane several times, always telling her of his love, while she was more concerned about his injuries and needed to know how they were healing. It was great to be in constant touch.

The night before the show, Jane rang reminding him that she'd not be at the farm at all during the two days of the show. He wished her luck and told her to take care.

The lorry taking the animals, bales of straw, hay, food etc., arrived at 6 o'clock in the evening; Jane and Arthur packed their kit-bags for their own necessary overnight things. The heifer went into the lorry quite calmly, but Monty pranced around for a considerable time before Jane finally got him in; she and Arthur sat in front with the driver.

The show was held in the medium-sized market-town of Thame, about 10 miles from the farm. It was an annual event that still managed to keep going even with the war on, and it was a one-day show. In the huge field, there were several large marquees, some housing rabbits of many breeds, bird varieties, and some

112

housing flowers and shrubs together with all kinds of garden plants. People were rushing about the site, finding their way around, and many were in the large beer tent, where one could also buy food and hot drinks.

For Jane and Arthur, once they'd discovered where the marquee for cattle was situated, it was all go as the unloading began. The two animals each had their own space in an open stall, and there were many others all of different breeds, along either side of this large marquee. All this made for plenty of mooing of varying tones. Jane tied Monty up in his allotted space, then she and Arthur put bales of straw all round him, and leaving him with water and hay they went off to do the same for the heifer. After seeing the animals settled, they themselves were ready to eat, and they found the beer tent packed with men and women of all ages; while Jane got drinks, Arthur went off in search of hot-dogs, which seemed to be all that was available. They tucked into a couple each, then from one of his pockets Arthur produced a bag of biscuits which his wife had made, and were they delicious! He told Jane, 'These are a favourite with my family and the wife thought we'd like some too.'

They parted afterwards to find their nearest 'loo,' and when she got back to the marquee Jane saw that 'the form was to wash in cold water using one of the cattle-buckets.' This she did, then like the other competitors, she wandered around to look at the opposition she and Arthur faced. There was a grand collection of magnificent cattle, and Jane soon got chatting to some of the owners. Most, she discovered, had not seen a Land girl before and there was much hilarity as well as admiration when she showed Montgomery to them. 'Only a girl could've called a young bull by that name,' they teased. 'You lot wait until tomorrow - he'll show you why I called him that!' She had wondered where they were to sleep but soon found out when Arthur handed her a palliasse plus an old army blanket; as she still looked puzzled he told her, 'We all doss down in here with the animals, Polly; so try to get some kip as it's a 5 o'clock start in the morning.'

Jane followed his example and was soon in a deep sleep - until the loud snoring from two farmers close by woke her with a start. After that she simply could not get comfortable and sleep was out of the question. The snoring, the smell and the lowing of the cattle, provided a truly unique experience in which she was pleased to be involved.

Jane must have finally dozed off because she was rudely awakened by Arthur rattling a bucket in her ear. She jumped up at once to find the whole marquee a buzz of activity. 'Come on sleepy head,' someone called, 'your young bull has got himself into a right old mess! It'll take you an hour or two to get him looking ready for the show-ring.' 'Don't sound so pleased about it!' Jane retorted, 'p'raps you'll be good enough to give me a hand later on?' She had a quick wash herself, again in a bucket of cold water, and Arthur brought her a cup of coffee and a hunk of bread and jam. She was so hungry she could have eaten almost anything. Next, she fed Monty and gave him some water, then putting on her Wellington boots and a khaki smock over her shirt, she began scrubbing down her charge. Talking to him all the time she said, 'After all the shampooing and brushing, you have to get into this mess! I'm ashamed of you Monty.'

An hour's hard work soon had him looking a champion again - at least in Joanne's eyes he did; for herself she felt hot, smelly and anything but the smart Land girl she'd hoped to look. All was not lost though: Arthur appeared with a clean bucket of hot soapy water and a towel. 'Couldn't have you letting that handsome young bull down by looking a mess yourself Polly, so get cracking with this.' Jane could have hugged him. She soon got clean and, while she was putting on the white smock, she saw, much to her amazement, Deborah coming into the marquee. 'Yes, it's me! Good old Frank thought I should come and support you, so I hitched a lift in a cattle truck and here I am.'

Once she'd got over the shock, Jane asked her pal, 'Don't suppose you've got such a thing as a comb in your bag, Debs?' 'Course dear girl. You know me! There's a mirror and face powder as well, so pop down to the lady's and sort yourself out.' Jane was mighty relieved, in more ways than one! She returned to the marquee in her clean yellow tee-shirt, hair tidied and even a speck of face-powder on her nose. The chaps soon spotted the difference, and there was plenty of wolf-whistling going on, for she really did look a picture. Her face was very brown and healthy-looking, her hair was blonded in front from days in the sun and she looked every bit a land girl with a purpose. Furthermore, there were now two of them!

The time had come for the judges to look at the cattle. First they were inspected in their stall area, then the best ones were selected to be taken out into the ring. This was an enormous roped-off part of the show-ground, where all kinds of events were held, including judging horses and sheep as well as cattle. There were seats all around this arena where the public could observe the various judging, and, later on, could watch the horse-jumping competitions. When her number was called Jane, led Montgomery proudly out into the arena, as did several other farmhands with their young bulls of various breeds. There was one other Ayrshire, a 12-month-old, who was almost all tan and dark brown in colour, while Monty was mainly white with only a few tan-coloured patches. Arthur had reminded Jane to talk quietly as she walked him around to try to keep his attention; but *he* had seen the others and hoped for a game! She tightened her hold on his halter so that she had more control of his actions; it was very hard work for her first time in a show-ring, and perspiration was running down her face and neck. Monty was a very strong and wilful young bull. After they'd been round twice the judges called four of them to the front, one being Montgomery, as well as the other Ayrshire and two Friesians. Jane's heart was pounding. Would Monty stand still? She sent up a silent prayer, but just as the judges moved over towards her he started to play up. The first judge asked her if she could possibly get him calm so that he could feel over his body: 'I can only try sir,' she replied smiling sweetly at him. Then Monty suddenly stood still, almost as though he'd heard her request. Jane answered all the relevant questions about his breeding and age, and then she was asked by the second judge to walk him 50 yards, turn and jog back with him. Monty was well used to this routine as he and Jane had done it over and over again on the farm. He rose to the occasion, obviously impressing this particular judge. After feeling, watching and assessing the other three young bulls, the judges conversed together for a while before they walked across to Jane. With smiles, they showed her the large red rosette, and each one shook her hand and congratulated her while the rosette was fixed on to Montgomery's head-collar - all amidst enormous applause from the public and also from the men she'd shared the marquee with. The two Friesian bulls were second and third, and all three were then asked to parade around the ring. It was then that things almost went very wrong for Jane: Monty thought it time for a game again and pranced about so much that she was scarcely able to hold on to him. Deborah suddenly rushed across to help, just in time, for poor excited Jane had hung on long enough and was near to exhaustion. Deborah grabbed the other side of Monty's head-collar, and between the two of them, the girls got him under complete control; he had had his fun and became as quiet as a lamb, enabling Jane to enjoy her first experience as a winner.

Back in the marquee, she told Deborah that she'd been a brick to go to her rescue: 'I really couldn't have hung on to him any longer. Thank you so very much.' 'It was your cowman, Arthur, who seeing your tussle shouted, 'for god's sake someone go and help Polly,' and I just took off.' After that they tied Monty up in his stall area, gave him some water and then headed for the beer tent. 'Drinks are on us' shouted several young farmers, 'that was a good show you put up there. You girls *are* pretty tough after all!' Jane was so proud she couldn't be angry with her naughty charge! 'He really did look handsome out there, didn't he Debs?' Her friend was as excited as if it had been one of her own, and after their drink they rushed off to find a phone-box so that Jane could tell Mrs Freeman her good news. The latter was as pleased as punch, telling Jane it was just reward for all the hard work she'd put in; she then added, 'Yet another cause for a celebration when I get home.'

The girls saw that the next to be judged were the 'in-calf heifers' and found themselves a good viewing place as the animals were being led into the ring. 'What is her name?' Deborah asked Jane. She replied laughingly, 'Actually it's Polly! She was one of the first calves I looked after when I went to the farm and they decided to name her after me.' Deborah then asked why they called *her* Polly, and she had to say that she had no idea, but had been called that since her first day there.

The heifer was very well behaved, and looked magnificent, her horns shining in the sunlight, her udder long and wide with small teats, just as it should be - she was due to calve at any time. 'It's really great working on a dairy farm,' Deborah told her friend as they watched Arthur's heifer selected out of a dozen others for the final judging; and Jane was getting excited at the thought of their going back with *two* red rosettes and could hardly contain herself. There seemed to be a long, agonising debate among the judges; it was between Polly and a shorthorn heifer. But finally the red rosette was pinned onto Polly's halter and the two Land girls were beside themselves with joy!

'This calls for another visit to the drinks tent,' was Deborah's comment, 'and this time we really will have a proper drink.' Two very merry girls rushed up to congratulate Arthur as soon as he had tied Polly up. 'You've been celebrating already I see,' he told them, 'we'd better go and have something to eat before loading ready to go home. It'll sober you two up a bit! But I must say I'm a mighty proud cowman today.' They ate some really hefty sandwiches of spam and cheese and drank large cups of tea with them. Then Jane said to Deborah, 'You'd better come back in the truck with us.' When they'd collected all the bits and pieces from the marquee, it was time to load the two animals into the lorry, which appeared right on queue. Arthur took 'Polly' in first and Jane followed with Monty - or tried to follow - but he was not having any. Deborah with Arthur tried pushing him at his rear, but to no avail: he simply refused to budge. By then, two chaps from the lorry next to theirs had seen their predicament and sprang into action to push with them. They were young and strong and almost lifted Monty from behind. He suddenly jumped on to the tail-board of the lorry, then gave another jump right inside, knocking Jane over in front of him. She struggled up and finally tied him so that he was unable to do any further damage, at the same time calling him a few unlady-like names!

On the drive back to the farm, Jane fell asleep; it had been a very long and exciting day. She woke with a start as Deborah said, 'Wakey, wakey, we're back.' Arthur told her to put Monty straight out in the field and he would see to everything else. Jane thanked him for a great experience, saying she would ring Mrs Freeman at once to give her the second bit of good news.

The following day was wet and Jane felt a bit flat after she'd completed her usual jobs. She took a look at Montgomery who was happily grazing away in the paddock, his beautiful coat of the previous day looking soggy and flat. He wandered over when she spoke, giving her his 'what a good boy am I' look.

Although by now Jane was pretty drenched as she went to fetch Blackie in, it was time for him to have some exercise she decided. In the afternoon, the rain fortunately eased a little, and she was about to go for a ride when the phone rang; it was Tom. She gave him all her news of yesterday, and the night before, and of course, he was very happy for her, saying it was well deserved. They chatted for quite a while - Jane asking how he was, sending her love to his family, and telling him she would write a letter to him that evening. Of course, she also told him how much she loved and missed him. She felt much better hearing that his burns were healing well and that the hair was beginning to grow again on the injured side of his head.

Blackie was eager to have a good gallop once they got to the field - which was now stubble - and Jane gave him his head; half-an-hour later, with the horse covered in lather and mud, she walked him slowly back to his stable to cool off.

After milking, she took the three dogs for a good walk around the fields on the farm, ending up near the water-cress beds by the cross-road leading to the RAF station. There walking towards her was a recognisable young, fair-haired airforce officer wearing wings on his tunic. She could scarcely believe her eyes: it was none other than Tom's brother, Nigel. He recognised Jane right away, saying, 'This *is* a spot of luck! Can I walk with you or would you rather I just pushed off?' Remembering the last time they met and parted, Jane was a little apprehensive; nevertheless she smiled and said, 'Of course you can walk with me, but what are you doing here?' 'The short answer is that I've been posted back to this station. I only arrived this morning and I thought I'd walk around while my kite is being serviced.' 'That's amazing! Have you seen Tom lately and did you know we are engaged now?' Jane asked him. 'The answer is no to both questions, but I do know he's at home right now, having had a minor accident of some kind. He's okay, isn't he? And my congratulations to both of you! Somehow I thought it might happen, but I hope you'll be sensible and wait until after the war is over before tying the knot.'

'We are being sensible, as you put it, Nigel. We both have our jobs to do and with Tom on operational duties, it's even more important that we wait.' 'I've just finished my third stint on ops and am actually here to instruct for a while,' Nigel told her. As they walked, he asked Jane if there was anywhere nearby that he could take her for a drink.. 'Just a little farther along past the lane to the farm where I work,' she told him, 'is a nice quiet place. I will meet you in there when I've taken these dogs back and fed them. It's called the 'Shepherds Hut', by the way.'

Feeling a little nervous about this idea, Jane decided to ring Tom at home to see how he felt. On the phone she said, 'Guess who I've just bumped into along the road? Your big brother! He's asked me to go for a drink with him, and I said that I would. Hope that's okay with you?' 'Why ever shouldn't it be? We've all been together before and you got on all right, didn't you?' Jane found she couldn't tell Tom about her last encounter with Nigel. The brothers were so close and so fond of one another. Tom, aware of the long pause asked, 'You do like Nigel don't you? He's not upset you in any way, has he?' Jane replied, 'No, of course not, and yes I like him. I simply wanted you to know that we were going for a drink together, that's all. When you ring tomorrow, I'll tell you how we got on. Bye for now, darling, and enjoy your time at home.'

Land girl Ch 15

After her telephone conversation with Tom, Jane went in to wash and change before going along to the Shepherds Hut. It was warm after the rain earlier in the day, so she donned shorts with tee-shirt and sandals. Nigel was sitting at a table outside the pub, seeming to be deep in thought as she walked up to him. 'Golly! I was miles away,' he laughed. 'Anywhere in particular?' asked Jane. 'No, just thinking ahead about what the future holds, and wondering what will become of us if we don't win this wretched war. Anyway, what can I get you to drink? Is it still lemonade shandy or have you progressed to something stronger?' Jane told him shandy would be fine as long as it was ice-cold, and, blushing slightly, she recalled the last time they'd had a drink together; she needn't have worried for fortunately Nigel seemed to have forgotten it, and they spent quite a pleasant evening.

She told him all about the agricultural show and other farming dramas; once more he told her it was so good to see her again, for she made him laugh and relax. This might be leading to dangerous ground she thought, as he left her to get more drinks. 'I have a very good friend on the farm, Susan. She is quite a loaner,' Jane told him when he returned. 'At present she is home on leave after a cycling accident in the black-out, but when she comes back we must get together.' Nigel gave her quite a quizzical look, 'Are you trying to match-make by any chance? There is only one girl for me and she is spoken for.'

Fortunately, Jane was saved from responding, as three of Nigel's pilot pals arrived and introductions had to be made, allowing her a little breathing space. The evening became quite jolly. The chaps enjoyed time off from the airfield, and found it good to be amongst civilians - especially girls. None had actually met a real Land Army girl before, and were interested in what she was doing and where she was working; the very mention of fresh eggs brought a sparkle to their eyes. Eventually, as dusk was falling Jane told Nigel she'd better get back; he wanted to walk with her but she managed to discourage him, and after wishing them all good luck she left them.

She did not go to sleep for some time. Things were playing on her mind, Nigel being one of them. Tom was very dear to her, they were now engaged, yet she still had Nigel on her mind; she was very fond of him in a sisterly fashion, but it was now obvious to her that he still loved her. But she loved Tom, so what was she worrying about? Nigel would never do anything to hurt his brother. Why, oh why, did he have to be posted back here? Many things milled around in her mind until eventually she managed to fall asleep.

The news on the radio the following morning was not good at all: many towns and cities had been bombed heavily with devastating consequences. For the people, like the people of London, life was almost entirely lived in shelters or in the cellars of their homes. Most of their children had already been evacuated to country places. Many got homesick and returned home. Rationing was getting tighter and the black-market was in full flow; even the meagre petrol allowance was denied the ordinary car user. The 'Dig for victory' signs abounded, and many folks kept a pig or two in their garden for fattening to supplement their meagre meat allowance. The battle for freedom was at its height and aircrews and ground crews alike were stretched to the limit.

Tom was now back in action; his burns were healed and it was only his hand which gave him trouble, particularly after a day's flying. Jane had to get used to not hearing from him all over again. She worked even harder on her vegetable garden and Mrs Freeman, now able to be home once more, was amazed at all it produced. With Susan back, the two girls worked hard hoeing in the field of kale which was shooting up fast and would provide much needed food for the cattle later in the winter. The remaining hens were not laying many eggs and when Nigel's pilot friends came one day to buy some, Jane had to tell them they could only have one dozen each. Prior to the culling, she had been able to sell as many as they wanted, to any of the forces. She had met Nigel for a drink on a couple of occasions, and he had behaved well, causing her no more sleepless nights. He said he enjoyed her company and felt he was looking after her for his young brother, which indeed he was.

Soon after Dunkirk, the Germans had occupied the Channel Islands. Jane had an aunt with two sons living in Alderney; her uncle was in the Royal Navy, and she guessed he must be mighty worried about his family. She decided she must ring her parents to see if they'd heard from them. Her mother told her that her brother's wife had said that all the lovely beaches were now sealed off with rolls of barbed-wire, that they were under curfew, and were constantly harassed by Germans. Food was short, and their once beautiful island now looked like a battlefield. Their two boys were made to work for the German army, and even their school had been commandeered for army use; there was little or no real life there anymore. It all sounded too depressing and once again Jane counted her blessings and felt that her hard work and long hours were worthwhile: simply to be free, at the end of each day, was indeed a blessing.

The clocks were altered once more and the days and nights became colder again. With darker mornings and evenings, life became even more dreary, but the work of the farm carried on just the same. The routine jobs of threshing, mucking-out, feeding and calving were with them once more. The cows were kept inside, and only Blackie and Montgomery were left in the field; those two had become great companions. On the plus side, Mrs Freeman was now fully fit, and riding again; she told Jane one evening that she was in the throws of buying a 4-year old mare for hunting. This news delighted her, as it meant another horse for her to look after, and she and her boss would be able to ride out together sometimes. The earlier purchase of more Ayrshire cows meant extra work for the three girls and Arthur, in the milking-parlour and dairy.

Because they were a tuberculin-tested herd, the perimeters of all the pasture fields used for grazing the cows, had to be double-fenced, and it was an almost endless job seeing that the fences were kept in good order. The use of electric fencing had just become popular, but they found it of little use to the fully-grown cows, because they very soon discovered how to lift the single electric-wire with their long, curved horns.

The arrival of the hunter for Mrs Freeman was a great occasion. She was a beautiful looking grey mare and looked the perfect ride for her. Jane was given the sole charge of her welfare, feeding, grooming, and stabling, together with keeping both bridle and saddle clean; she still did the same with Blackie's tack, bridle, saddle and harness whenever it had been used. Mrs Freeman re-named the mare Tonie; she'd apparently had a horse with that name long ago which had meant a lot to her.

Jane was due some leave, and in a letter to Tom she was able to ascertain that they could spend some of it together; he was well into his second operational tour and had been granted a short break. Luckily this coincided with Jane's time off, and reluctant as she was to hand over her charges to others for ten whole days, she could hardly contain her excitement that she and Tom would be together again at last.

Before this happened, however, she and Susan went to a village dance. During the interval, in walked Nigel with the three friends Jane had already met. On that previous occasion, Jane had worn civilian clothes and it was quite a few minutes before Nigel recognised her. Once he did, he rushed across the room to her, 'Haven't we met before somewhere?' and proceeded to whisk her off onto the dance floor and Jack, his friend quickly grabbed Susan, and one way and another a good evening was had by all. They adjourned to the refreshment room eventually, Susan looking flushed and happy; she whispered to Jane that Jack was a good dancer and also she told her friend that she could see the likeness between Nigel and Tom. As the men went to collect refreshment for them she added, 'He seems very smitten with you Jane! It's a good thing you are engaged to his brother.' Their evening ended with them going home together; as they walked, they all sang together, such tunes as, 'We're going to hang out the washing on the Siegfried line', 'There'll always be an England,' and 'We'll meet again, don't know where don't know when,' and to the latter Nigel gave Jane's hand a quick squeeze. 'Goodnight and good luck,' said the girls as they went up the lane to the farm. They could still hear the pilots singing as they went on up to the aerodrome.

Jane filled Tom in about their evening out, the very next time he

126

rang as she wanted to keep nothing from him. They arranged to go to her parents' for the first two days of their leave, and this turned out to be a happy reunion with her family. Tom met them all at long last. Before they left, Jane's father produced a bottle of 'bubbly' - a friend had found it in his cellar, and 'no questions asked!' He wished them both every happiness, and much good luck, which he knew they would need. Her sister, Kathleen, joined in the toast, telling Jane, 'You've beaten me to it after all, kiddo!' When they were leaving, her mother added a rather tearful 'goodbye and God bless you both.'

This time, it was to Tom's home in Dorset. He was still able to get petrol and although by now it was pretty cold in his little sports car, both were warmly clad and enjoyed every moment of the drive. Arriving at his home, they found all very quiet, even though they were expected. Dashing up the stairs two at a time, Tom called out 'Are you there mother?' A white-faced Mrs Gregory appeared from a bedroom, 'Hello, darlings! It's so good to see you.' 'What's up Mum?' Tom asked, seeing his mother's solemn face, 'I'm afraid it's your Gran, she is failing fast. I'm so glad she has lasted long enough to see you - she has been asking about you and Nigel.'

They went quietly into the room, where Gran seemed to be asleep. Tom went up to her and kissed her forehead, and she turned slowly, murmuring, 'Tom, you did come after all.' Then her eyes closed again, but she gripped his hand tightly and he felt he must stay there with her. Jane understood, and she and Tom's mother went down the stairs to the kitchen; there she asked Mrs Gregory how long grandma had been like this. 'Mother seemed to give up after Nigel's last visit,' she was told, 'and even more so when she didn't see Tom for so long.' Then brightening up a little, Mrs Gregory said, 'His scars seem to have healed beautifully - even the injured hand. Thank God; we were so worried, and I'm sure you were too.' Jane said vehemently, 'This bloody war, it's no wonder poor gran can't take any more! She does look extremely frail, but perhaps seeing Tom and knowing that he's here will help a bit - and help you and Mr Gregory too. Does Nigel know she is dying? You do know he is stationed right near where I work?' 'Is he really? We didn't know exactly where he was. Have you seen him and is he well?' 'Yes to both questions. We met quite by chance when he had only just arrived, and we've met once or twice since.'

Changing the subject, Jane asked if there was anything she could do - any shopping, preparing food? 'Thank you dear, my husband does the shopping and I've got the evening meal ready to put in the oven.' She then told Jane that the doctor had said there was nothing more he could do for her mother; she was a tired old lady and could slip away at any time. 'Not much of a welcome for you and Tom I'm afraid, but we knew he would want to see her,' she said sadly. Jane put her arms around Mrs Gregory, saying, 'We're both glad to be with you just now.'

When Tom came downstairs later it was obvious that he'd been weeping at the thought of losing his much loved grandmother He asked Jane if she would go with him for a short walk. At that moment, his father came back loaded with groceries, Tom ran out to help him; Jane saw them fondly embracing one another and felt so pleased that they were all here together at this sad time.

Later Tom asked if he should try and get hold of Nigel. 'It's difficult to know what to do. We know he's back in the thick of things again, but what we don't know is how much longer your gran will be with us,' his dad replied.

Tom and Jane went off to walk for a while, Jane not knowing quite what to say, Tom being obviously very upset. 'Why did I think gran would go on for ever? I've been selfish not thinking about her or making the effort to come and see her more often.' 'Don't say that Tom! You've had your job to do - your gran knows that, and she wouldn't want things any other way; it's lucky we came when we did, and at least it's a comfort for your mother.' They ambled along and later found themselves at the 'local.'

'Let's drop in for a drink shall we, love?' he asked Jane. Inside, the landlord asked after 'that grand old lady' as she was known locally. Tom told him that sadly she was slowly slipping away. When he ordered a beer for them both, the landlord said, 'It's on the house lad. We all admire what you chaps are doing, and are pleased to see you've recovered from your accident.' Then looking at Jane he added, 'We've seen this lassie before! Yes, a Land Amy girl as I remember. Another one doing a grand job! Here's to both of you, and good luck.' Tom replied, 'She is engaged to me now, but we're both feeling so sad that my gran is unlikely to still be around for when we can get married - which won't be until after the war.' 'You'll make it, lad, especially having this lovely lass to come back to,' the landlord said cheerfully. They stayed for a while, Tom talking to various people he knew as they came in. They held hands but talked little; it was a sad homecoming for them.

Jane offered to sit up with gran that night, but Tom wouldn't hear of it. 'I've done little enough for her these past few years.

At the very least I can sit with her during the time I am here.' His parents were obviously relieved at his offer for they'd been sharing the nightly vigil and both were in need of sleep. Tom spent the time stroking the old lady's forehead gently, and in the early morning Jane found him asleep with his head on her pillow; she woke him saying she would take over while he showered and got some breakfast. 'Do everything as quietly as possible, darling, your parents are dead to the world, so let them sleep as long they need.' Tom said, 'You are a love! How many girls would give up their precious days off sitting with a frail old lady?'

Later that morning when Mr and Mrs Gregory were up, Jane told them sadly, 'I don't think your mother will be with us much longer. Would you like Tom and me to go and fetch Nigel?' Her reason for saying this was that while sitting watching and listening to the old lady, Jane had noticed the greyness of her skin, and heard the slow rasping of her breathing; she remembered long ago, when her own grandmother was dying, seeing the same symptoms.

During the morning, after he'd been with his mother for some time, Mr Gregory decided he would try to get through to the aerodrome. Tom told him to ask for the Adjutant, explain the position, and if Nigel wasn't available, ask someone to get a message to him to ring home as soon as possible. It took a long time for his father to get through; eventually he was told that his son was airborne, but they would get the message to him as soon as he landed.

Jane asked Tom's mother if she could go and look at gran's garden, but added that if anything needed doing she'd stay and do it. Tom walked along with her and took the keys so that he could look around inside; although her helper did still go in once a week he just felt he wanted to sit in her cottage, it held so many memories for him.

They set off, both well wrapped-up for there was an icy wind blowing; neither spoke much, knowing that gran could die at any moment, and someone very dear to them all would no longer be around. After she'd seen what needed doing, Jane opened the tool-shed and got out a hoe to set about some weeding and removing flowers long since over. The lawn that was, had become long and overgrown, but there seemed little point cutting it at this time of the year. The vegetable garden was full of every kind of weed which she also tackled. Tom came out eventually to give her a hand and they at least made it look tidy; he told Jane his gran would be pleased it would not seem left uncared for. They locked everything away before leaving, and, taking a last look, set off back to the house with heavy hearts, thinking they'd probably never see the lovely old place again. Stopping off at the pub, Tom rang home to tell his mother they would eat lunch there. He also asked if they'd heard yet from Nigel, but so far they hadn't.

Some friends of Tom's dropped by for a pint, all asked about his gran. One of the older and wiser villagers said kindly, 'You must be thankful for her life. Don't mourn her death when it finally comes - she made her mark in this world all right I can tell you. Used to be always active, always busy, but never one to listen to gossip, a rare quality for anyone in such a small village, I can tell you.' Jane felt near to tears. Everywhere she'd gone around this part of the world, gran was spoken of so highly; she hoped she'd be able to follow her example in her own later years.

After dinner that evening, Nigel rang and his mother told him that his gran was slipping away. He told her he could only manage a 48-hour pass. He asked if he should he come now, and if she would know he was there? His mother said she certainly knew Tom was there, but only for a few moments, because as she grew steadily weaker, she kept falling asleep. Nigel made a quick decision: he would drive down and be with them later that evening. A bed was made up for him in his old room with Tom, and his mother made sure that a meal would be ready for him. Jane and Tom went for a short spin along the coastal road, and stopped at a small inn where they sat looking across the sea. They drank ice-cold beer, neither wanting to speculate as to how long their dear gran could hang on. Tom said, 'I just hope we are all together when the time comes. We hear about chaps being killed day in and day out, yet nothing really prepares us for when it's one of our own.'

'Don't distress yourself Tom,' Jane told him, 'she has had a good life, and my guess is she is ready to die. And remember what that lovely old boy in the village said this morning. Just think of what a happy life she has had and be thankful for her that in her final hours she has all her loving family with her.'

It was quite late when they got back. Tom's father said, 'I think you'd better go up my boy, the doctor has been and says the end will be tonight.' As Tom rushed two-at-a-time up the stairs, Jane heard a car pull into the drive, and the next minute Nigel burst in: 'I'm not too late, Dad, am I?' were his first words. His father shook his head, and like his brother, Nigel dashed up the stairs.

Some long time later they came down: 'It's all over. She is at peace now,' Mrs Gregory said, putting her arms around her husband. Tom turned to his brother saying, 'You just made it, I think she was waiting for you, Nige, and at least we were all with her.' Jane quietly asked if anyone would like a cup of tea. Nigel looked across at her, 'Sorry, Jane, I hadn't even realised you were here, and yes, I for one would love a cup, and I'm sure mother would.'

Land girl Ch 16

The next few hours were not easy for Jane. On the one hand she was pleased to be there giving help and support, yet on the other hand, she felt rather an intruder in such an intimate family sorrow. She helped by preparing meals, tidying the house and doing any shopping that was needed. She comforted Tom whenever they were alone in the only way she knew – she hugged him, held him and let him talk. His parents were busy making the arrangements for the burial; unfortunately, Nigel would have to leave once his 48-hour pass was up. He said that if possible he would be back when the date of the funeral was fixed, and he gave Jane a special hug and kiss before he left. He told her what a godsend she had been for them all at this sad time. She was touched by this for she realised how very hard it was for the boys as well as for their parents.

Tom was able to get extended leave in the circumstances; he and Jane managed a few daytime excursions around Dorsetshire, but a deep sense of loss accompanied them all the time. Tom was able to talk about his childhood days, when he spent holidays with both his grandparents; he remembered the happy times they had had, which now seemed so very long ago. Mrs Freeman added two extra days to Jane's leave after hearing about the family's bereavement. She knew that Jane desperately wanted to be with Tom for the funeral, which was being held in the village church that gran had attended all her life; she had asked to be buried next to her husband. Apparently she had asked Mrs Gregory, when she knew her time was running out, to make it a happy occasion, not a sad one, in thanksgiving for the wonderful life she had enjoyed. She had firmly stated '*no tears*' and 'lots of flowers, please'. Jane felt the former would be quite difficult for she had been loved by so many - not only by her close family.

The day dawned sunny after a hard overnight frost, which apparently was unusual for this part of Dorset. The previous day, Tom managed to get buckets of flowers from every garden in the village: late flowering chrysanthemums, galardias, coloured berries and a variety of foliages which Jane, and local ladies gran had known, arranged all around the church. Mrs Gregory and Jane worked non-stop the following morning preparing for the gathering expected at the house afterwards; Tom and his father dealt with drinks, glasses, and chairs. At 2.30 precisely, the service began. The small church was packed to overflowing - family, friends and villagers, all paying their respects to a wonderful lady. Sadly, no Nigel, they thought. But as they moved to the graveside there he was, standing alone, head bowed, looking like a lonely little boy; yet at the same time, he also looked every bit the officer that he was in his uniform. His parents smiled across at him, pleased that he had managed to get there. Both boys stood at attention as they saw the coffin lowered; then they stepped forward together to throw a handful of earth on to it. They moved back, one on either side of Jane, who at that point, could not hold back her tears.

At the house she was kept very busy knowing that Mrs Gregory had many friends and relatives to greet. Tom and Nigel supported their father as he too moved amongst all the people. Eventually everyone left and the mammoth task of clearing away and washing-up began. Over a hundred people had attended and Tom, thoughtful as ever, sent his mother up to her bedroom to lie down - she was looking totally exhausted. They suddenly noticed Nigel was missing; he too was asleep on his bed having driven down straight from a night of fighting the battle in the air.

Jane eventually went up to see him; again, she thought he looked just like a little boy with his fair hair ruffled, hugging a very ancient scruffy-looking teddy-bear. She smiled, put a blanket over him and quietly left the room. Later when she told Tom and his father where he was, Tom laughed telling her that he always went for his bear when he was unhappy about anything, and a good sleep right now was what he needed more than anything.

Next morning Nigel seemed to have recovered a little, and after he had eaten a good breakfast he said goodbye to his mother and father. Putting an arm round his brother, he wished him 'all the luck in the world,' and with a quick glance at Jane said, 'I'm sure you've already got that in your Land girl. You're a lucky chap.' Tom also wished his brother 'all the best' as they walked out to the car together.

When he got back, Tom said quietly to Jane, 'I do believe my big brother is jealous of me having such a wonderful girl, and before it gets forgotten, thanks a million for all you have done, all your love and care looking after mum and dad, and if I've neglected to tell you this past few days, I *am a lucky fellow having a wonderful, caring girl like you.* '

They both had to leave the following day, and it was a pretty sombre drive back as they were aware that they might not see one another for some time. Also, they were both only too aware that Tom would be going back to operational flying. Now the battle was against the German nightfighters that flew night after night against British bombers as they attacked German war sites and cities. All the air-crews continued to suffer heavy losses even though the RAF now had lots of young men completing training, and keen to go into action against the foe.

136

Back at the farm, threshing was again in full flow: the same dusty job, the aching fingers caused by throwing sheaves to the appropriate position, the back-aching job of moving the heavy bales of straw, not to mention the extreme cold. Jane and Susan were thankful they had more milking and dairy work, which meant less time on the threshing machine. They had harvested a bumper crop of wheat as well as barley that summer; consequently, the threshing went on a lot longer than the previous year. Jane and Mrs Freeman enjoyed riding out together whenever they were free, and Tonie proved to be an excellent mare and a very good jumper. Her owner, now completely recovered, was once more a member of the South Oxfordshire Hunt, which gave Jane yet another interest. Her duties now included not only tack to clean more often, but more intensive grooming of Tonie; also, she was in charge of cleaning out the stables and the horse-box. Frank always made sure there was plenty of hay and straw for her use, and often gave a hand in the mucking-out when the weather prevented tractor work in the fields.

Evenings were spent as they were the previous winter, the girls going dancing or playing table-tennis with the service men from the local airfield; Deborah joined them whenever she was free. Jane had heard from Tom that he was now on a course preparing to fly as a night-fighter pilot as more planes for this job became available. In strict confidence, he told her they were called 'Beaufighters,' that there would soon be more squadrons of them and that he was hoping to be a Flight Commander in one of them. Jane told him she had heard from his mother that all was well with them. She had asked Jane to let Tom know – when he got in touch with her – that his grandmother had left her cottage to him; to Nigel, she had left a large piece of land in the same village. Tom was silent for a moment, then said 'Bless her, she always said she would do that, but I'd forgotten all about it. Would you please ring mother for me, and tell her I'm okay - just extra busy right now, but will be in touch shortly. I love you, Jane darling. Take good care of yourself.'

That evening Jane rang Mrs Gregory with Tom's message. His mother told her that Nigel had now got another overseas posting: he was to go on active service in the Mediterranean where the allies were having a tough time in Italy. So it would be some time before they could all be together again, but she hoped Jane would go and see them if and when time allowed.

The winter months dragged on. People continued to enjoy the Christmas season when it came, although Jane missed Tom terribly; but so it was for millions of wives and sweethearts, and the war was still far from being won. On the farm, calves continued to arrive and the previous ones were now almost young heifers. A big blow came when Arthur announced that the time had come for Montgomery to be sold at auction. He asked Jane if she would care to take him but she declined - she couldn't possibly be there to see him go. Susan offered to do this instead, as he was so used to a girl handling him. Jane remembered vividly when he had had a ring put in his nose: two men and the vet had trouble, but as soon as she appeared, he became docile enough to enable them to do the job.

After the Christmas, period Jane went home, where she once again enjoyed the local New Year's Eve ball, meeting lots of old friends as well as family. She was saddened as she remembered the previous year when both her cousins, home on leave from the RAF, were there, and most of all, her close friend Mick had been there. Her parents were pleased to have her home, and to hear all her news; her sister, too, was glad to see her. Her parents already knew about Jane's engagement to Tom, and both felt sorry for her that she saw him so seldom; they liked him immensely and continually prayed for his safety. But now other things were on their minds, their Land girl was about to have another birthday. Arthur and Dobbin's wives were planning a surprise party, to be held in the village hall. They had contacted the RAF band, and through Mike, the pilot Jane had befriended, it was arranged that they would play for the evening. He had been very pleased to hear from Mrs Freeman since her time in hospital, and asked endless questions about Jane and Tom, because naturally they had lost touch with one another since Tom's posting.

The big day arrived and when Jane came downstairs that morning she was greeted with shouts of 'Happy Birthday!' Everyone on the farm had gathered in the kitchen. She was completely unprepared for all the attention: everyone gave her a card, and Benny shyly held a bunch of flowers behind his back until Dobbin gave him a nudge saying, 'Well, aren't you going to give 'em to Polly then?' Just before they all disappeared, Arthur said, 'We'll all see you later.' When they had filed out to get on with their various jobs, Jane said to Susan, 'How did they know? Who let the secret out, was it you?' 'Not exactly, but tonight all will be revealed, so let's get over to the cowshed and begin the milking or the poor creatures will be bursting their udders!'

Laughing happily, the girls donned their warm jackets and off they went. Mrs Freeman had been very quiet all morning and Jane remarked about this to Susan: 'Ah! Well! I think she has something 'up her sleeve' for later today,' was the reply. Both girls went off to cut kale after they'd had breakfast, taking the dogs with them. It was cold work at first but they soon got used to it and warmed-up by hacking away at the thick stalks. They saw the postman cycling down the lane on their way back, and he waved, shouting, 'One of you lasses must have a birthday I reckon?' Jane fed the dogs, then the horses before going into the house, by which time Susan was like a cat on hot bricks, dancing around the kitchen. 'Do come on and open some of this mail! It's just about all for you, and the suspense is killing me.' The very first card was a beautiful one from Tom, followed by cards from Jane's family, Tom's parents, Deborah and several other friends; there was also a lovely one from Pat and Bob, and then a somewhat flush-faced young lady read one from Nigel, who sent his congratulations and love, all the way from Cairo. Jane was very touched at receiving all these, yet very slightly puzzled that she'd not had one from Mrs Freeman herself.

After they'd had their lunch her boss excused herself saying, 'I'll be back in a second - don't go away.' Suddenly Jane heard horse's hoofs outside the door. She looked out to see Arthur and Mrs Freeman leading a beautiful chestnut filly, and as she rushed out her boss gave her a big hug and handing her the halter: 'A very happy birthday from all of us at the farm. We hope you will enjoy breaking-in this young lady as much as we will enjoy watching her progress. She is all yours, with our love and thanks for all your hard work here. You've been with us a long time, Jane!' Poor Jane was completely overwhelmed. Tears poured down her cheeks as she said, 'Thank you, thank you all so much,' over and over again. Looking at the little filly, she could see that she now had a thoroughbred all of her own. She was all chestnut, apart from a white diamond-shape on her head; Jane

140

guessed she was not yet a year-old.

'Wherever shall I keep her? Blackie and Tonie have the stables!'
'Ah! but that's all sorted,' Arthur told her, 'take a look next door
where you used to wash and grade the eggs.' Lo and behold, it
had been completely re-vamped into a beautiful clean, light and
warm stall for one - hay already in a net and fresh straw
underfoot. Jane still seemed in a complete daze, 'Oh! what a
wonderful birthday present! I simply can't believe this beautiful
animal is for me!'

At every opportunity during the rest of the day, she looked in on
the filly, such was her excitement. She and Susan discussed
several names for her, but so far none seemed quite right. 'I will
have to study her pedigree papers and see if I can come up with
an inspiration,' Jane decided.

When the girls finally went in, Jane noticed no table had been
laid for their supper; there were no pans or cooking smells of
any kind. She looked at Susan who was trying not to laugh: 'We
must both go and put on our party dresses for that's where we
are all going! Mrs F. has arranged everything, so come on.' 'A
party for me as well!' Jane thought there was no end to the
surprises that day. She had a quick bath, then got out her one
and only evening dress and put it on, thinking as she did so, 'I
wonder where it is being held?' Suddenly a car-horn sounded
and out the two girls rushed. It was Jane's father, her mother and
her sister! There were lots of hugs and more birthday wishes as
well as presents, and finally they all drove off, down to the
village hall where the girls had so often been to local 'hops.'
When they arrived, Jane was amazed to see such a crowd already
there. The usual chant of "Happy Birthday To You," met her as

she went in. She scarcely recognised all the men from the farm, all dressed in their Sunday best once again. Also, she saw her aunt, uncle and even one of her cousins in his RAF uniform; then there was Deborah and her latest boy-friend, several friends from her school-days, both male and female, and many chaps from the local RAF station. Some she recognised and some she vaguely remembered from her egg-selling days. Altogether it looked a very large crowd, and she even spotted some local farmers and their sons, wives, and daughters. Then she saw Mrs Freeman, looking very elegant in a long blue velvet dress. She was looking pleased that her surprise party was obviously making her Land girl very happy indeed. The RAF band was on the stage and began playing 'Twenty-two today,' following it with a quick-step tune inviting everyone on to the dance floor. There was a rush for Jane, of course, and Mike was the winner; he whisked her away in the crush. 'How did you all manage to be free tonight, and how were you all contacted?' she asked in bewilderment. 'Don't ask so many questions! Just make sure you have a wonderful evening - that's all that matters,' he replied as they danced happily around the room.

For Jane, the whole evening was magic; in fact, the entire day had been just that. When they finally got home, after at least a whole half-hour saying goodbye to everyone, Jane straight away went up to Mrs Freeman. Putting her arms around her, she thanked her for such a memorable day, and for all the arranging she must have done. Tearfully, she said, 'I will never forget today as long as I live, and I can't wait for the morning to see my little filly again.'

Land girl Ch 17

Jane was up by five the next morning: she had something on her mind, the something being her chestnut filly. She drank a quick cup of tea, then pulled on her woolly hat and warm jacket, and went across to the stable. As she opened the door, there was a tiny nicker as the young animal struggled out of the straw bedding to her feet; she was not at all afraid of this strange girl and nuzzled up to her as if to say 'I'm hungry.' Jane fed her straight away, then cleaned out the stall, put fresh straw down and filled the net with sweet-smelling hay, which the colt began to tackle at once. After looking her all over, Jane decided she simply had to find the right name for her. Her coat was beautifully shiny so she had obviously been well cared for (a winter coat does not usually become shiny without a lot of care). She decided that she would put a halter on and lead her up the lane for a little exercise as soon as she had a minute to spare.

Milking seemed-never ending that morning; the newly born calves took even longer learning to lap their milk, with or without her help, and she still had Blackie and Tonie to feed and clean out. While they were having breakfast, Mrs Freeman asked if she'd thought of a name yet; she and Susan made several suggestions, but none were quite what Jane wanted. They advised her not to rush over her choice, because something would suddenly come to her, and be just right for the filly.

Later that morning, Dobbin asked her if she would like him to give her another ploughing stint, using two of the cart-horses; he said she should use the quieter Bess and her usual partner, Smokey. This was a wonderful opportunity for Jane to advance her ploughing skills - she had long admired the grace of the cart-horses as they slowly plodded along, pulling a single furrow plough. Dobbin told her, 'Put some heavy boots on, Polly, and then come to the stables yonder and I'll let you harness them.'

Five minutes later, she had joined him. He told her 'this is just to remind you what us 'as to do 'Fust thing is to know which is the 'arness for the job. It's bridle, collar, 'ames and a pair of long trace chains. Them we attach to the front of the 'ames and at the rear to an 'ook. Long reins is used to drive the 'osses from behind the plough. Now, let's see if you can 'arness 'em.'

This was no problem for Jane other than that she had to get a box to stand on since both horses were many hands in height; but she soon managed to complete the job. Taking down two nose-bags filled with chaff plus some chopped mangolds, Dobbin hung them on to the hames along with his own haversack containing his lunch. He gave Jane a leg-up on to Bess's back, and using Smokey's mane, pulled himself up on to his back, and off they went. When they reached the field, Jane asked why horses were being used and not the tractor. 'Well, to start with, you can see as 'ow Frank is already using it over in yon field and t'other is that we'm going to use a lea plough, whereas Frank is using a three-furrow unit plough, which covers the ground much quicker.' Jane had to be content with this explanation as Dobbin busied himself fixing on the plough-share; then he attached the two horses to it before they set off to cut the first furrow. It had looked a fairly easy job for the man behind guiding them, but Jane knew from her first attempt just how difficult and tiring it could be!

The horses knew their task, there was no doubt about that. They walked so that the small land-wheel stayed on the unploughed land while the large furrow wheel ran in the bottom of each furrow. They kept a very steady pace; even so, walking with one foot lower than the other became very tiring. Dobbin was pleased with Jane's effort, and when he noticed her tiring, he advised her to have a break while he carried on.

After three years of having Land girls on the farm, the men had come to fully appreciate that they would give all they'd got to any task they were asked to do. Dobbin was particularly fond of 'Polly' who had been there the longest; he knew that she would not give in unless he told her to. She ploughed several more furrows with the two horses and after a while had again got the hang of it; she was less tense now that she was holding them back to her own pace. It seemed no time at all before Dobbin called out 'time for grub.' Jane set the two nose-bags, one on each horse, and went off back to the farmhouse, having said cheerio and thanks to Dobbin.

She caught a lift back on the tractor as Frank was on his way home. He asked, 'How did the legs stand up to it?' She had to admit to being 'damn tired', but glad to have tried it again after all this time. 'I'd like to do it again another day,' she told him. He smiled and said that ploughing with horses made a much better job than using the tractor; he then asked Jane if she'd noticed the absolute precision of each furrow, both in width and depth.

Mrs Freeman was anxious to know how she'd got on also, and wanted to know if she'd be too tired to ride out with her before milking began. Although Jane was vehement about not being too tired, she found climbing into the saddle, with Blackie anxious to be off, was not quite as easy as usual! They had a good ride, with a gallop or two, across the still unploughed fields. Tonie, with her long legs, easily outran Blackie whose legs were her fairly short; as usual, she tried valiantly to keep up.

After milking that afternoon, Jane went as usual to feed the newly-born calves. To her horror, she noticed that one didn't attempt to get up - it was lying with its neck fully stretched-out in the straw. She dropped what she was doing and tried to rouse the little mite but there seemed no sign of life at all. She rushed over to get Arthur, wishing he would hurry instead of walking at his usual slow pace. He took one look at the tiny creature and shaking his head said, 'I'm afraid that's your second casualty Polly, there's nothing we can do. .It's just another unfortunate loss I'm afraid; I'll get old Benny to bury it right away.'

That evening, Jane told Mrs Freeman she had a name for her filly. 'It's to be 'Nanna', after Tom's grandmother - a lady I loved dearly in the short time I knew her. It was also Tom and Nigel's childhood name for her.' Her boss said she approved thoroughly for she knew Jane would love and care for the filly, just as she had Tom's gran. Before it got too dark, Jane put the halter on Nanna and walked her along the lane, letting her look around and get familiar with her new surroundings. When she had bedded her down for the night, she heard the phone ringing and went indoors just as Susan was about to call her. It was Tom. After quite a long chat, she returned to the sitting-room to tell her boss that Tom was being sent to Italy shortly, where he would be flying either Spitfires or Hurricanes; he would have a few days' leave before going and hoped to spend time with her. She didn't seem as depressed as usual about his posting, and Mrs Freeman felt glad that Jane was getting used to these things happening; she felt so pleased she'd given her the filly - it would keep her busy and take her mind off Tom's news.

It did just that; every spare moment Jane had was spent either grooming or exercising Nanna, and she vowed that as soon as spring came she would start to break her in. Meanwhile, Tom had come and gone, with the promise that when 'all this is over, you and I will get married and live in the cottage grandma left to me.'

Sadly for all concerned this was not to be. On the 28th of February, Tom was killed in an air accident. His mother sobbed over the phone, 'Jane what can I say? Please ask Mrs Freeman for some time off, and come down to us as soon as you feel able'.

Jane was totally stunned; she could not believe that this was anything other than a terrible nightmare. After she had put down the phone, she shut herself away in her room feeling that life was over for her without Tom.

She remained in her room for four days, hardly eating a thing. Messages came by the score but nothing could take away her pain. Susan, Deborah and Mrs Freeman did all they could for her and tried to tempt her with meals. She thanked them, but could not eat. Her parents came and went, but they seemed unable to get through to their devastated daughter. They were feeling just as stunned as Jane.

Eventually, Arthur came up with an idea: 'It's not a very fair one for our girl, but we've got to do something and it might just do the trick', he told his boss. When he and Dobbin had been leading Nanna out one day for exercise, she became lame; it

147

seemed a stone had got caught in her hoof and it needed to be removed. They had both tried but the little filly would not let them near enough even to hold the hoof, let alone try to remove the stone. 'It needs either the blacksmith or getting the vet out,' they said, 'but Polly ought to be told first'. The next time Mrs Freeman went up to Jane with some hot soup, which was just about the only thing she would take, she gave her the facts as gently as she could. It was as if she'd exploded a bomb, there was such an immediate reaction!

'Thank God,' she thought. Jane got into her clothes for the first time in four days, bounded down the stairs and out to the stable. She talked to Nanna quietly, as always, for a few moments, gradually getting closer and closer until she was finally able to stroke her neck without her backing away. It was obvious that she'd been thoroughly frightened, most probably because of the pain, but also because the one person she had come to trust was missing. After several minutes, Nanna allowed Jane to lift the hoof which by now was quite swollen and hot. She put it down gently, and going into the house, collected hot and cold water and a sponge. Next she asked Dobbin if he would give her a hand, which he was only too pleased to do. He was gentle with Nanna as she knew he would be, having watched him with his cart-horses. When Jane had put on the halter, he held the filly, still talking softly all the time while Jane first bathed the hoof in hot water, then cold, followed by hot again. Finally, as she gently lifted it, she was able to see the offending stone, well embedded in the red swelling. She decided there and then to get the vet out as she had neither the knowledge nor the tools to extricate the stone herself. Dobbin was in full agreement with this. The vet was unable to come right away but said he'd be with them by teatime. Meanwhile, all this had brought Jane out of herself and her grieving, for a while at least.

Later that day, over in the cowshed, Susan and Arthur were preparing to start milking. They both looked up as Jane appeared, neither one of them knowing whether to mention their sorrow for her or not. She forestalled them both saying, 'I know how you feel, just as I feel, but we *are* in the middle of a world war, and life right now is unfair to many, not just to me. I *will get over Tom's death*. It's going to take a while, so please bear with me if you can.'

They both thought what brave words from someone so young, and who had obviously been so very much in love. Her companions were quiet during the milking, deep in their own thoughts, and full of love and respect for this girl in her bereavement. Throughout the days that followed much help, love and thought was shown to Jane by all on the farm. The vet had successfully removed the stone from Nanna's hoof, and given Jane instructions about the after care, which he thought would be speedy on such a young and healthy animal.

When the day arrived for Jane's departure to Tom's home, Mrs Freeman, now able to drive again, took her to the station in the car promising, for about the hundredth time, that they would all look after Nanna with great care. As the train got closer to Poole station, Jane got more and more anxious. How was she going to cope with the sympathy she would be getting and the sympathy she would have to give? Her eyes filled with tears, even before the train stopped; she shook herself, knowing that she had to be strong for Tom's parents - stronger than ever before.

Land girl Ch 18

The train, going into Poole station, seemed slower than ever as Jane's anxiety mounted. The last meeting with Tom's parents had been for grandma's funeral, an old lady who was ready to die; this time it was to talk over their son's death, her beloved Tom, who was only twenty-three, with all his life before him. She began to weep silently, her loss and the sadness of it all suddenly overwhelming her once more, and she was thankful to be alone in the compartment.

Suddenly, the station was there. Jane gathered up her bag and small case, sighed deeply, and prepared for this inevitably, very sad meeting. Nigel was there to meet her train; he looked weary and forlorn, although being very tanned made him look well. He gave her the usual hug, but no kiss this time. Once inside his car he turned to her, putting an arm across her shoulders, saying sadly, 'Jane this is one hell of a thing to have happened to two wonderful people. Even my own loss cannot possibly match up to yours.' 'Thanks Nigel, I know how close you and Tom were, and *you* had known him all your life, whereas we had such a short interrupted time together. But oh! I loved him so much!'

Choking and distraught Jane wept freely. Nigel was in tears also, as they clung to one another for comfort. 'Let's get home,' he said at last, passing a large handkerchief to dry her tears, then using it to wipe his own tears away. With the familiar village coming into view, Jane asked him if he was on a normal leave; he said that it was a kind of 'compassionate' leave to be with his parents, but, he added, 'They knew on the squadron that I'd be useless at my job right now, so that's why I'm here.'

150

Mrs Gregory met them as they drove up to the door; she looked very tired and pale, 'I'm glad you could come dear, we need each other so much at this time.'

Nigel left and went off to put his car away, at the same time telling himself that now he must be strong, and most certainly hide his own feelings for Jane; he knew he must try to be positive for her sake, especially as he could see how the loss of his brother had really hit her. When they had finished tea and settled down, he turned to Jane asking if her parents had known Tom. 'Of course they did, and they are sad for all of us; they sent their love as well as their condolences.'

His next question was about the farm; this was a good move as it seemed to cheer everyone up hearing about her filly, about the name she had chosen for her, and about her second effort at horse-ploughing. She told them how kind and considerate everyone on the farm had been and that she could stay here with them as long as she felt needed. Mr Gregory, who had hardly spoken, suddenly said, 'They sound very loving people to me. That's what comes of working on the land and with animals. Your boss has had her fair share of problems as well as coping with the loss of her husband. It seems this war is touching and hurting everyone, no matter where or who they are.'

After a while, Nigel asked his mother if she had had any further word from the RAF with regard to Tom's burial. His mother, looking drawn and desperately sad, said she had heard little other than that many of his squadron friends had been present when they buried him; obviously, this had had to be done quickly due to the terrific heat out there. Nigel seemed more than a little puzzled about this, and asked, 'Would you like me to try to find out more? At least it might help a little?' 'If you would dear,' his mother replied, 'I presume he would have made a Will and the Adjutant would probably know about that. He said he would be sending all Tom's papers and belongings as soon as possible. We also hope to have a photograph of Tom's grave and to know exactly where it is, so that one day..... maybe...... ,' she couldn't go on. Jane could scarcely bear to hear these things although she knew they had to be discussed; asking to be excused, she went up to her room.

Once there, she again burst into torrents of tears, seeming almost unable to control herself, saying over and over, 'Oh, Tom! Why did this have to happen to such a wonderful person as you. I miss you so much. I can't seem to pull myself together, I keep thinking and remembering all our love, the good times we shared and all our plans for the future.' She lay on the bed, shaking and exhausted, until she finally slept. When she woke up some hours later she could hear someone knocking on the door. It was Nigel, and as he walked into the room he could see her red and swollen eyes, and his heart went out to her. It was all he could do to stop himself enveloping her in his arms, but summoning his good sense, he simply asked if she would like to come down for dinner. With a great effort, Jane pulled herself together and told him she'd be down in a few minutes.

In the dining-room, all eyes turned towards her as she walked in. She managed a smile and thanked them for waiting, saying she did feel rather hungry as she'd not eaten for several days. The meal was simple, as wartime meals usually were, but she enjoyed the food and the company; she felt at one with them as they all suffered this tragic loss.

Afterwards the conversation lightened and was mainly about the village annual fete which the Gregorys were involved in. As Tom's father pointed out, 'Life has to go on, others have had their losses as well as us.' Brave words and true, but they helped no one there. While Jane helped Mrs Gregory with the dishes, she asked if Nigel had been home long. 'No, he only arrived early this morning,' she answered, 'this has been a shocking blow to him, he and Tom have been so close all their lives.' Jane left the kitchen abruptly, rushing outside into the garden where her tears and sobs seemed to tear her apart again. She staggered about not quite knowing where she was. After some time Nigel found her, again red-eyed, white-faced, and this time almost hysterical. He pulled her into his arms, at the same time talking gently to her and lowering her into a seat in the garden. 'What has upset you so much more?' he asked. She mumbled inaudibly something about, 'How can I mourn him properly, with no body and no grave here?' Nigel was shattered; he'd not really given much thought to the fact that to Jane, as to them all, there would be no funeral or burial for his brother, as it had already taken place. He stood up shouting loudly, 'This bloody, bloody war! We've all seen so much, too much. But, Jane, we have to go on accepting it, and you *must* try to do that as soon as possible. You must carry on with your life.'

Nigel stayed for a few more days; he told his parents that once they had received all Tom's effects and knew all the details of his accident and the whereabouts of his grave, they must take a short holiday, and also try to carry on with their lives. They agreed to do this, knowing it made sense, and they promised to let both him and Jane know as soon as they'd got any further news.

Nigel and Jane did a lot of walking and talking. She learned a great deal more about Tom, and her terrible heart-ache seemed to ease off a little. She found in Nigel a true friend and admired the way he was coping with his own great loss, and how valiantly he was trying to cheer everyone up. She also knew that he was dreading going back to whatever his own fate might be. Before leaving, he took Jane down to the 'local,' and even though it was painful to both, somehow it seemed to put things in perspective knowing that they simply had to get on with their lives. She thanked Nigel for this, and then asked him where he would be stationed now. He told her he was again on fighter-planes, but this time at an airfield near London.

He left the following morning. He offered to drive Jane back and drop her off at the farm because he was flying back to his base from the airfield at Benson, but she declined his kind offer. She felt that it was too much for them both to leave his parents at the same time. Mrs Gregory was especially grateful to her, for she really wasn't feeling ready to get back into village life just yet. Jane busied herself in the garden and after doing all that seemed needed she went for a walk to take a look at the cottage grandma had left Tom. She was very surprised to see how lovely and how cared-for the garden was. Standing there looking at it, she remembered all the plans she and Tom had made, and thought about how they would so much have enjoyed living there together. But it was not meant to be.

Jane somehow realized then that because she'd come here and thought about things, she *would* now be able to go away and cope with life; nothing could take away all her happy memories of knowing and loving this wonderful family and their two sons.

Four days later, having phoned her boss, Jane went back to the farm. Everyone was pleased to see her and to note that she seemed to be in charge of her life once again. Nanna looked quite beautiful, her coat shining like silk; apparently, she hadn't taken too kindly to the menfolk either walking her out or grooming her, but out of the blue, Susan had offered to take over, telling them that she knew the routine. She had watched and listened to Jane so many times. It warmed Jane's heart to know that she had taken such care of her filly, and to see that Nanna seemed fond of her too. She gave Susan a special hug and in thanking her, tears came to her eyes; she was just so overcome that this girl, who only a short while ago was terrified if a cow moved when she was milking, had found enough courage to take on the not yet year-old colt, the pretty, skittish Nanna. All the same it was a wonderful moment for her when her precious animal whinnied loudly as she went into her box, and nuzzled up to her. It was these small things that made her feel good, and realize that she had not been forgotten.

Springtime came around once more and once more the countryside came back to life. The cows went out during the day as did some of the young stock. Nothing seemed to have changed on the farm, and yet it had; it all showed Jane that life went on no matter what, just as the war went on..... and on. There was more bombing, more lives lost, more saddened families at home and abroad, killing and dying were a way of life. Once more, Nigel and his safety came into her thoughts; the Gregorys simply could not face the loss of another son, and yet she knew, should it happen, they would.

Benny became ill, all of a sudden - so ill that he was taken to hospital. Mrs Freeman, knowing that he had no family, was a constant visitor, never going to see him empty-handed. On her first day-off, Jane also went to see him; she scarcely recognised this tiny wizened old man, yet his eyes told her that he knew her immediately. He even managed to hold her hand and say in a weak voice, 'I'm so sorry for ye Polly.' This brought tears to her eyes, but with a great effort she managed a 'thank-you Benny, I'm sorry seeing you like this. Is there anything at all I can bring you?' A weak voice replied, 'Just me 'baccy and pipe.' Jane spoke to the Sister before leaving and learned that Benny's heart was not in good shape at all, and as for smoking, oh no! News on the war front was that on April 16th, the island of Malta was awarded the 'George Cross' because of the heavy bombing it had endured and for its bravery under terrible circumstances.

Susan and Deborah now often went along to the village local 'hops,' just as Jane had in the past; both had become very popular, these blue-eyed blond-haired young Land girls who were also excellent dancers. They told Jane that some American airforce boys had cycled from a village not too far away, where their base was set up. They'd heard about the dances that were held quite often, and came to investigate. The two girls amused Mrs Freeman and Jane by telling them how they all chewed gum non-stop and were not at all slow to pick up the girls! Susan told them that she and Deborah were very quickly snapped-up by two of the USA master-sergeants, and Jane smiled at all this chit-chat; she was pleased that both were enjoying their time off work.

She thought that maybe some day she too would begin to go out again, but the loss of Tom was still very much with her. In fact, work on the farm was a great blessing because somehow she felt nearer to him here. Jane spent many hours not only with Nanna but with Blackie also; she felt she'd neglected her rather since the filly had arrived. Now she would saddle her up, and with a leading rein on Nanna, the three of them together with the dogs would ride around the farm's perimeter. Up until now she had not introduced the filly to any traffic other than the farm tractor; she played up quite considerably the first two or three times when they met it, but by now mostly ignored it, much to Frank's amusement.

On the work side, there were still plenty of new calves arriving regularly, and her heifer-family was quite a large one by now. Montgomery, now almost three years old was in great demand, but he still always preferred that Jane was with him when 'duty' called! Arthur had not had the heart to take him for auction as he'd intended; he felt that Jane needed things to remain the same for a while.

After she'd been back from Dorset a couple of weeks, she got a letter from Mrs Gregory telling her about Tom's accident, which apparently had happened in the air. He had been flying over the desert when he'd been caught in a severe sand-storm with very high winds; finding himself low in fuel, he had tried to get back to base, but had not made it. On his forced landing attempt, the fuel ran out, causing him to nose-dive into a deserted tank. His aircraft must have burst into flames on contact, and Tom, unable to get out, was burned to death. Mrs Gregory told Jane they said it would have been instantaneous, and they were sure that he would not have known much about it. His plane was not found until two days later, and on investigation, the facts of the accident became apparent.

The last part of the letter told Jane that Tom had left all his possessions to her, and of course, these included grandma's cottage; she and her husband both sent their love to her and hoped she would contact them when the reality had sunk in, and when she felt ready to discuss it all.

Jane talked over her news with Mrs Freeman, who told her not to rush but to leave things as they were for the time being; when she felt ready, she should either go and see Tom's parents or write to them. At present, Jane felt nothing but horror about the crash, and began to have nightmares about it. She eventually became so exhausted that she had to visit the doctor who prescribed sleeping pills. After several nights taking them she began to sleep better, and soon other things took her mind off the letter with its news of Tom - at least for a day or two.

The hospital contacted Mrs Freeman to say that Benny had died peacefully in his sleep; they asked her to go to see the Almoner there to make arrangements for his burial. Everyone on the farm met to discuss this. It was sad for them all, not least for Dobbin who mostly worked with Benny, and also drank a pint or two in the local with him on a Saturday night. The general consensus was that he should be cremated and his ashes spread on his favourite spot on the farm. Mrs Freeman said she would make the arrangements.

Everybody from Blackbush Farm attended the Service, as did many other local farmers and village people. Benny's old cap and pipe rested on top of the coffin. Donations were sent to the local "Home for old and Retired Carthorses" as a tribute to Benny; these animals had been a major part of his life. In the evening, all the workers from the farm met in Benny's local and drank a toast to this gentle and very much loved man.

The cremation service had a profound effect on Jane, for somehow she felt Tom's presence with her there. Later, after talking about this to Mrs Freeman, she felt that now she had really come to terms with her loss. For the first time in weeks her spirits began to lift. Meanwhile, Jane's mother seemed to think that it was time they saw their daughter again and rang telling Jane that they would be glad if she could go home on the following Sunday for lunch to see them all. She said that she would as it was her weekend off, and they chatted on for a while; it dawned on Jane that her mother was also checking to see how her daughter was coping with her recent loss.

The remaining months of 1943 seemed to fly and soon things were all to change again as the winter months approached.

Land girl Ch 19

News on the war-front was that Great Britain and America were now on the offensive in all theatres of the war. The Americans had gained great victories and Japanese forces were on the retreat in many areas of the Pacific. But there was a long way to go before the aggressor nations were well and truly beaten.

Jane had worked almost non-stop since both Tom and Benny had died; she had got very run-down and was constantly getting colds and sore throats. This was unusual for her since she was basically a very healthy girl. Mrs Freeman and Arthur told her that all her jobs could easily be covered at this time of year by Frank and Dobbin, or Geoff, Dobbin's eldest son; the latter was officially a farm worker, and therefore exempt from conscription.

Feeling very much under-the-weather, Jane agreed to have some leave. Susan said she wanted to look after Nanna, Blackie and Tonie, as now, towards the end of the year, the cows and young stock were all inside; thus things were set in motion so that her jobs were done during her absence.

Jane went to see her parents first of all, but her thoughts were so much with Mr and Mrs Gregory, that, after a couple of days, her mother suggested she might make use of Tom's car, which they'd kept in their garage, and use it to drive to Dorset. Her parents' friends all contributed petrol coupons to enable her to do this, and she then needed no further persuading. On the next fog-free morning, she set off. This time her spirits rose as she neared the Gregory's village; she had finally accepted her situation and begun to live again.

The house was very quiet as she went along the drive - no Mrs Gregory at the door to meet her, even though she knew roughly the time Jane might get to Poole. This seemed most strange to Jane, so she went in calling, 'Is anyone at home?' Finding no one in any of the rooms downstairs she went slowly upstairs, quietly calling again. This time, the door of Mrs Gregory's room opened and a nurse appeared, beckoning her into the room. Quietly, she told Jane that Mr Gregory had suffered a stroke the previous day. At this moment, his wife was sleeping in the chair by the bed; she had scarcely left his room since it happened. Jane slipped quietly in, and looked at these two people who were so dear to her. She had tears in her eyes as she kissed them lightly on the forehead before leaving the room.

The nurse followed her down stairs, where a tray of tea and scones was set, and she told Jane they were for her. Apparently, Mrs Gregory had tried hard to stay awake until her arrival, but sleep had finally caught up with her. Jane asked, 'What actually happened to Mr Gregory?' The nurse told her that he'd collapsed yesterday morning and the prognosis from the doctor was that it was quite a severe stroke; however, it would take a day or two before they would know just how much he would be affected. Mrs Gregory had asked that he remain at home unless the doctor thought otherwise. He had agreed to this as long as she had nursing help, so that was the present position. Jane thought 'thank goodness I've come' as she went up to her usual room and began to unpack.

Some time later, there was a tap on the door and Mrs Gregory walked in. 'Oh, Jane! It's so good to see you, but I'm sorry you've found us in trouble yet again - it all happened so quickly, right out of the blue.' 'I'm glad to *be* here,' she replied, 'and I'm terribly sorry about Mr Gregory. You must be so very worried, but at least now I'm here, I can help.' 'But you are here because of your own ill-health, and I'm not letting you do too much. The nurse takes care of my husband and you will be good company for me. I'm *so very pleased to see you and have you here, Jane.*'

Although there were anxious days following his stroke, Mr Gregory was well cared for, with day and night nurses coming in. On the ninth day, the doctor told Mrs Gregory that he was afraid her husband was paralysed down one side of his body; it was possible he may never walk again. The doctor had known the family for many years and knew that this good lady would want to know all the facts. Even so, this news was a terrible blow: it left her with so many decisions to make, at least until her husband regained his speech, and even that was not a certainty. One decision she did make right away was that Nigel must not be contacted while he was still on operational duties; time enough when next he got home.

Jane took Mrs Gregory out almost every day, either walking or for drives in the car. Many visitors came to see her husband, a very popular person who had always been there to help other village people in their own hour of need. After she'd been with them for two whole weeks, Jane felt much better in herself and wondered about returning to the farm; but given the circumstances, Mrs Freeman told her there was no rush. All was going well at the farm and she thought Mrs Gregory's need was the greater. The invalid began slowly to regain a little speech and was eventually able to be downstairs, in a wheel-chair. Consequently, only a physiotherapist was needed daily and the nurses were able to leave. This cheered Mrs Gregory up as she felt in charge once more. As it was near to Christmas, Jane was able to take her shopping while her husband had his daily treatment.

'If you feel you can cope now, I think it's time I went back to work,' Jane said to them one morning. Mrs Gregory said, almost apologetically, 'We've kept you away from your own work long enough and are so grateful for all you've done for us. You must be longing to get back to your friends as well as all your animals, and with a daily help coming in we will be fine.'

Before leaving, Jane told them, 'Please don't hesitate to call me if things get on top of you. Being here has given me back my own health, so don't forget. God bless you both, and thankyou for everything.' As she hugged her, Mrs Gregory said, 'You are like a daughter to us Jane, the daughter we never had, and it's we who thank *you* for being here and cheering us up.'

With those kind, loving words she made her farewells to them, and set off back to the farm once more. Her journey was without incident and it was just on tea-break time as she went into the farm-house. Deborah, Susan and Mrs Freeman were all there. After telling them her news Jane went upstairs to change into her working clothes, then straight away out to see Nanna and the rest of her charges. When they saw her, the farm workers told her they were pleased that she looked her old self once more. Jane said that she was glad to be back, and that she would gladly work over the Christmas break for any of them, 'But don't all ask me on the same days!'

This meant that Susan was now able to go home to see her family. Since Deborah would still be there, Jane was free to pick up more or less where she'd left off, helping in the cowshed, feeding the calves and the older stock and dealing with horses and dogs as before.

It was back to freezing-hands time, apart from in the dairy, where it was always cosy; outside, cutting the kale in the fields was the real killer. When it was just frosty with no snow Jane rode Blackie and had Nanna on a leading rein, but her feet got very cold, and occasionally she would dismount and walk with them in order to get her circulation going.

Several evenings later, she rode home on her bicycle to see her parents. Their news was mainly regarding Kathleen who was now engaged to her American airman. She wanted to have a New Year wedding, for which plans were now being made. Jane sensed right away that her father was not too happy at the thought of the eventual outcome once the war was over. When Kathleen came home, she was positively glowing with happiness; she tried to keep herself in check, knowing that it would bring 'everything that might have been' back to Jane. However, Jane was very happy for her and agreed to be her bridesmaid when the time came. When Kathleen's fiancé, 'Dusty', arrived, he hugged Jane and told her how sorry he'd felt over her sad loss. Needless to say, it turned out to be a very happy evening with lots of chatter and fun. Later, when Jane and her father went out with the dog, it began to snow, and he asked her if she should stay the night. 'Dad we are short-handed as it is. Furthermore, I've just had a lot of time off, so I must get back, and you know perfectly well that I'm used to cycling in all weather. Now I'll get my coat on and be off before it gets too thick.' Hugging her mother and sister, a shyish hand-shake for her future brother-in-law and a big kiss for her dad she set off into the white night with just a flicker of light, as usual, from her cycle lamp. It was not quite as cold as the ride down had been but as the snowflakes got heavier, she soon began to look like a snowman. There seemed to be absolutely no one else out on this night, but it didn't worry her one bit, used as she was to country life.

All the same, she was glad when the farm lane appeared, although hearing the dogs barking as she approached, Jane knew something must be bothering them. She called to them to be quiet but their barking still continued. After putting her cycle in the barn, she let them out of their kennels and unusually, tonight they just rushed past her and round to where the remaining hens were housed. Jane grabbed a torch from the kitchen to follow them, and to her dismay saw several headless bodies; bones and feathers were scattered all around, and her torch showed her the culprit's footprints in the snow. Yes, it had been a fox. She assumed these lifeless bodies had been the stragglers who had stayed underneath the house instead of going inside. The dogs came back to her after chasing across two more fields; they were very wet and bedraggled after their fruitless run to catch the killer, but as they seemed to expect some kind of praise from Jane, she fondled them saying 'good try, better luck next time.' With that she took them back, rubbed them down, and fed them.

By this time, it was well after 11o'clock, and Mrs Freeman was waiting up wondering whatever was going on. She was not as distressed at losing some hens as she was at the sight of her very wet and bedraggled Land girl; she'd heard the dogs barking but thought they'd simply missed being fed and were barking to remind someone. While enjoying a drink of hot cocoa, Jane told her about her sister's forthcoming wedding and all the plans that were being made; by then she was almost falling asleep - the cocoa and the warm kitchen after her cold cycle ride had finally wearied her. She climbed the stairs to bed.

Going out to the chickens the following morning, she noted that most of the dead carcasses had disappeared and thought another visitor! The dogs were with her and they too knew another prowler had been around. They began sniffing and whimpering and generally getting themselves into a lather, dashing here and there. Jane said not a word to anyone else on the farm, not knowing just who had been responsible for shutting them up the night before. She told herself 'it was really my job, and someone else had had to do it in my absence.'

Christmas came and went with Jane holding the fort again. She was glad to do so since she knew she would need time off for the forthcoming wedding. She did go to the New Year's Eve ball at the Officers' Mess with Susan and Deborah, as all three had been invited. Susan had come back from her leave especially for it. Jane's father had delivered her evening dress to the farm in good time, and had brought all the other bits and pieces her mother thought she might need. Susan had been given a long dress as a Christmas present, and Deborah already owned one. They were quite excited as they dressed up that evening. Susan's current young man was a Squadron Leader whose invitation had come with a note telling the girls he would fetch them in his car. 'You all look very lovely', Mrs Freeman told them as she offered each of them a glass of sherry to toast in the New Year and to wish them a very happy evening. It put them in good spirits, and when Jack, Nigel's squadron leader friend arrived, he too joined them all in a toast for 'better days to come.'

Once they were signed in at the guard room, all was set for a lively evening. They had drinks at the bar and then the buffet supper, with goodies the girls hadn't seen for many a day. Afterwards, the dancing began. Jane had wondered if she would know anybody there but it didn't seem to matter as there were plenty of more-than-willing dance partners. She did feel a little sad when the singer in the band sang the tunes Tom used to sing to her, but it was only momentary. Everyone was so friendly that she really couldn't feel that way for long. Jack was an absolute angel, introducing her to all his unattached friends, and when he finally got chance, he too danced with Jane.

During one such moment he talked about Nigel, asking her if he was any relation to Tom, as they had the same surname. He knew all about her sad loss from Susan and felt he could ask her this as it had been on his mind. It had been well over a year now, since her fiancé was killed and Jane found that she could talk about Tom once more. In answer to Jack's question, she told him that Nigel was indeed Tom's brother and that he was at present in North Africa.

'Not now he isn't!' was the reply. 'He is back in England, probably at home with his folks right now.' Jane looked quite staggered at this news, but managed to smile as she said, 'I'm so pleased to hear that he's back and *safe*. His parents will be overjoyed, for his father has been quite ill. Thanks for telling me, Jack.'

All to soon it was midnight and everyone held hands to sing 'Auld Lang Syne', wishing one another a 'Happy New Year'. It was now January, 1944. The war still raged on, leaving more and more families with missing, or believed-killed relatives and friends. But this *was* a party night, and those in the mess carried

167

on with the festivities - streamers, balloons, fancy hats and lots of merrymaking. Both Susan and Jane were beginning to wilt a little. Around them, several armchairs had two occupants, one with Deborah and partner in, both asleep with their party hats all askew. Jack remarked that there'd be lots of sore heads that day, and asked Jane if she had she enjoyed it all. 'Most certainly I have! I've made many new friends tonight, and you've been so careful to see that I've not been left alone, always introducing someone to me.' Jack smiled as she followed this saying, 'Susan is a lucky girl finding you, and I'm just so pleased for her. She was rather left out of things for a time.' 'She is a great girl and fun to be with, *and I may say,* is extremely fond of you. I felt that I knew you even before we met tonight, she's sung your praises so often.'

Jack, together with one of his friends, escorted the girls back to the guardroom to sign them out once they finally managed to wake Deborah up. Then they all piled into the car for their ride back to the farm. The girls kissed their two escorts goodnight and thanked them for such a lovely evening. As they were going in, the young officers asked if they were they going to start the milking right away. Susan laughed, 'We might just as well, it's hardly worth our going to bed for only one hour!' With that, the boys left, both waving crazily out of the car window.

'What a wonderful evening,' Jane told her two friends. 'Are you properly awake Debs, or shall I do your milking for you?' In the end, all three decided to change out of their finery, have some breakfast, and make an early start on their chores. Both Deborah and Susan were just a teeny bit giggly after all the merry-making, having had far more drinks than they were used to!
All the cows had their milking machines on when Arthur finally

appeared, not looking at all his usual composed self. 'Have we got a bit of a hangover then?' Susan asked him with a grin, 'Just a big one, not a bit of one,' was the hoarse reply. 'Well you can go back to bed, we three will cope, *we don't have sore heads,* do we girls?' 'You speak for yourself, I'm not feeling *that* perky, but we will manage Arthur, it's not often *we* can help you - usually its the opposite! So off you go,' Deborah told the sorry-looking Arthur, who was still holding his head. The girls were highly amused to see 'old sober-sides' as they called the cowman, in such a state. They finished off all the work, feeling ever so slightly smug! By the time afternoon milking came around Arthur seemed fully recovered and everything returned to almost normal - Deborah was found fast asleep on her bed, and therefore it was Jane and Susan who took her place, before Arthur could make any comment!

Land girl Ch 20

The days simply flew by, and life at Blackbush was governed by the land, the stock and the farming calendar. By this time, Jane had got all her young heifers, together with some younger calves, up on Rumbold's, in the same field where her chickens had once been. After hay-making finished, Dobbin had built a rick there which he'd surrounded with barbed-wire to prevent any animals helping themselves. On this particular day, Jane was to take a load of the hay back down to the farm and she'd harnessed Prince into a hay-wagon for this purpose; once there, she needed to remove some of the wire to gain access to the rick. Her young stock, always nosy when anything unusual appeared, ran over to inspect what was going on, and once satisfied carried on contentedly grazing the new grass away across the field.

It was a beautifully clear day, with a great deal of flying activity from the aerodrome: Spitfires were in and out, re-fuelling rapidly and taking off again. Most of the heifers ignored the noise of the aircraft but the younger ones cringed a bit if planes flew very low. Prince was quite calm though, and Jane managed to pile a good half load on to the wagon before jumping down to give the horse a drink from the churn of water she'd brought along with her. Then, sitting down on the far-side of the rick in the shade, she drank tea from her flask. For just one moment there seemed to be perfect peace. It was shattered suddenly when she heard the splutter of a Spitfire's engine as it swooped very low right over her head; it sounded rough - as though it was in some sort of trouble. The very next minute, she saw that the plane had made a forced-landing across the other side of the field, almost in the hedge. To her horror, she saw her terrified animals running off in all directions. Prince remained reasonably calm, simply twitching his ears. Most certainly the Land girl was *far* from calm: she was extremely scared of what might have been, and, in her fear, became angry. Her anger sparked more when she saw the pilot scrambling out from his cockpit, presumably quite unhurt. The two of them met as *he* was walking over towards the horse and wagon and *she* was on her way over to give *him* a piece of her mind – a mind which was very near to boiling point by then. Stopping a short distance from her, the young-looking pilot, whose face by then had become very red, started to apologise; he'd hardly said his first word when he was met with, in his words, 'language, such as he'd never heard before, except in the presence of men.!'

Calming down a little, Jane asked, 'What the devil were you playing at?' She threw her arms about pointing to her fleeing animals, angrily adding, 'it will take me hours, if not days, to collect them from wherever they end up. What a bloody-fool thing to do!'

Relenting somewhat, she looked at the young flyer asking, 'You *are* all right, I presume?' He assured her that he was. Seeing the rueful smile on his face she deigned to listen when he quietly told her, 'I was air-testing this Spitfire after a service and, as you can see, things aren't quite right. In fact, I had no other option than to get her down into the nearest field and unfortunately it happened to be this one. I'm very sorry to have scared away all your cows.' Jane replied, 'Well I suppose it couldn't be helped in that case, but incidentally they are not cows you've scared all over the countryside, they are Ayrshire heifers and calves - pedigree ones at that!'

For a moment they eyed each other, and, as her belligerence

died, the pilot said, 'My name's Peter, will you tell me yours?' Jane remained silent, still stunned by the whole event. Peter added, 'I have to stay here 'til someone arrives from the airfield because there will have to be a guard on my 'kite' until it can be removed. Before I go, can we shake hands and call a truce, and will you please tell me your name?' Jane relented, having simmered down; she had also noticed again just how very young and tired the poor chap looked. Holding out her hand, she told him, 'I'm Jane, known on the farm here as Polly. I can hardly say it's been nice meeting you in the circumstances, but I wish you well all the same,' and with that she offered him a drink from her flask, which he accepted gratefully.

As they parted company, Peter returned to his 'kite' to await the arrival of crash crew and ambulance, while Jane had to finish loading the wagon. At least she did give one or two thoughts to the poor chap who, she thought, had probably had quite a fright. Perhaps she'd been too harsh and unkind when all he'd done was to try to save his aircraft from destruction by landing it in the nearest field?

On her way back, she was able to find all the heifers who were feeding along the grass verge; however, knew she would need Bess's help to get them back up in to the field, particularly since they seemed very content grazing where they were. Jane carried on with the load, back down to the farm. Arthur told her she'd been plenty long enough getting the hay, but when she'd told him what had happened they began to plan a search for the animals as soon as milking was finished.

Next she fetched Bess, and getting on her bike, set off to round-up the heifers before they wandered off too far. Fortunately, as they were familiar with both Jane and the dog, this did not cause her too much trouble, and she finally got them all safely back in the field. All that was left to bring in were twenty-four calves! When she went into the house for her cup of tea, the first thing Mrs Freeman said was that some van driver had called by to tell her he thought some of her calves were along the back road heading towards Benson. 'They couldn't be ours surely?' she asked. Jane responded, 'I'm afraid they may well be, I'll explain all about it later, but right now I'd better find Dobbin and Frank - I just hope they've not already gone home. I need them to help get the calves off the road and into a field,' Jane explained.

Getting back on her bike once again, she saw Frank putting the tractor away and when she'd told him the story, he said he'd get his bike right away. He said that Dobbin had just that minute gone along to his home, 'You'd best fetch him! The more the merrier when dealing with scared young stock.' As the three cycled almost into Benson village without seeing any sign of the calves, Jane began to wish she'd ridden Blackie - then she could've gone across the fields where they'd most likely be, for she knew they'd be even more scared if they saw any traffic. It was quite late and they'd cycled through Roke and Berrick villages, when a young lad Frank knew asked if they were looking for some white and brown calves. He confirmed that they were and the boy told him where he'd last seen them, 'But they were movin' some,' he said. Off they went once more, down a lane which lead to a disused quarry where they finally found the unhappy animals huddled together, looking very dejected. 'Polly you'd best go up to 'em first as they knows your voice, us don't want to scare the poor cratures any more,' said Dobbin wisely. Jane spoke quietly as she approached and they looked up knowingly, as if to say, 'we know that voice!'

There they were, all twenty-four, and as she slowly walked behind them with her arms outstretched, they began to move back up the lane. Dobbin and Frank decided that as Polly was in control now they'd do best to cycle on in front in order to keep the animals moving along the road, and to keep them out of any fields. It was a long way back, and seemed even longer as they had to be very patient with their charges, still scared from the events of the afternoon. Eventually their patience paid off and they reached the lane to the farm. 'Us'll put 'em all in young Monty's place for tonight, Polly, if that's all right with you?' 'Okay. Anywhere as long as they are safe,' said Jane wearily. 'And thanks a lot,' she told them as they were leaving, 'I'll buy you both a pint in your local - that's a promise.' 'Night Polly, glad we got them back for you,' Frank shouted as they cycled off to their homes.

Afterwards, she told both her friends and Mrs Freeman about the dreadful language she'd used to the airman, which they could well imagine, for Jane could get herself very worked-up if her precious animals were in any danger! Her boss said much later that evening, 'I think we'd better have a glass of sherry. You've obviously had quite a long, tiring day, and an early night seems appropriate. What do you girls think?' 'We heartily agree, and let's hope we don't meet this poor fellow on any of our jaunts into the village,' Susan remarked to Jane.

That night, once she had got into bed, the Land girl began to feel quite ashamed about the way she'd spoken to the tired-looking Spitfire pilot. Alas, for her, fate was to intervene. Susan's words came flooding back to Jane a few weeks later, when the girls were dancing in the village hall. It was almost ten o'clock in the evening when Deborah, Susan and Jane were sitting out, having danced for most of the evening, when three young pilots walked in, somewhat unsteadily.

As they stood looking into the crowded room, Susan noticed her friend stiffen and try to hide behind her. 'What's up Jane?' she asked. 'It's *him*! The chap I swore at the day his plane landed amongst 'my girls,'' she replied. 'Don't worry he hasn't noticed you, and anyway they seem to be making for the refreshment room. They're probably in need of some black coffee by the look of them!' Deborah remarked typically, 'All the same they look quite interesting don't you think?'

Several weeks later, Jane went to another village hop - this time with her old school friend, Sally. The 'jitter-bug' craze, introduced by the Americans, was at its height on dance floors all over the country, and Sally was an expert at this. Not so Jane, who watched with amazement at the acrobatics of jitter-bugging and all the antics that this type of dancing involved. Suddenly she heard a voice saying, 'I believe we've met before but in slightly different circumstances, and if I remember rightly the name is Jane and.. er.. Polly?'

Standing there looking at her, was Peter, the young pilot she had sworn at so vehemently when his spitfire had crash-landed. 'Oh! It's you,' she said, 'have you and your friends sobered up a little now?' 'Looking a bit sheepish he told her, 'There was a reason for our going a bit over the top that first night we came here. We had lost three of our friends on operations that day. It was not a celebration, just the opposite - we each drank a pint more than normal to their memory *and* we all suffered for it the following morning when we had long trips over Germany. It can get very cold you know, and at the altitude we fly to avoid enemy flack, it's freezing, and when one's had a lot of beer the night before it can be jolly uncomfortable. Do you understand what I mean?'

Jane nodded smiling at him, as she suddenly realised what he was telling her. Being Jane, she next asked a straightforward question: 'What *do you do* when you need, you know, when you need to relieve yourself?' Peter then felt obliged to tell her of his predicament once when his cockpit windscreen had got iced up. 'Ah!' Jane replied as his plight began to dawn on her.

When a slow foxtrot began Peter said, 'Dare I ask if you would have this dance with me;' and when Jane agreed they proceeded to dance with absolutely no animosity between them. Jane was later laughing at something Peter told her, 'Ah! that's better - it's the first time I've seen you smile or laugh.' The ice was broken as they finished the dance. Peter rejoined his friends and Jane went back to Sally who looked at her saying, 'You've obviously forgiven the unfortunate fellow then?'

The two girls noticed that the pilots had vanished soon afterwards, and decided it was time they parted also. Sally worked in a local factory where they made the wings for Spitfires and she had an early start, just as Jane had.

Cycling back to the farm, the Land girl thought about her meeting with Peter; she even thought how cold it must be flying at 30,000 feet in order not to be spotted by the enemy and it made her realise that her cold job on the farm or out in the fields, in winter, was not *so* bad after all. She had never given a thought to the plight of aircrew flying long missions in inadequately heated aeroplanes.

The girls didn't venture into the village again for several days as they were sharing the jobs with the men so that everyone had some time off. Having been home the previous weekend for her three days' leave, Jane decided to visit Dorset and Tom's parents once more. She drove down on Boxing-Day in Tom's car; it was bitterly cold, but at least not yet snowing. Mr and Mrs Gregory were delighted to see her, and, putting her arms around them, she noticed how much better the former invalid looked, and how greatly his speech had improved. Although still in a wheel-chair, he was mentally very alert, with his wife looking her happy self again.

Going into their sitting-room later, Jane saw Nigel, who jumped up right away, giving her the usual peck on the cheek. It was then that she noticed a lovely girl, in RAF officer's uniform, getting up out of one of the armchairs and walking over to her, 'You must be the wonderful Land girl I've heard so much about!' 'Yes, this is our Jane,' Nigel told her. Then to Jane, 'Meet Geraldine, she's a member of my squadron. After the introductions the two girls chatted away like old friends, and nearer lunch-time, Mrs Gregory asked Jane if she'd care to give her a hand in the kitchen. During their conversation Jane said, 'I'm so pleased to see Nigel with a girl-friend at last.' His mother was silent for a while then replied, 'I was worried that he still carried a torch for *you!*' 'Believe me, I'm more than pleased - as well as relieved – that he's found someone at last', Jane replied.

'What about you, have you found a nice young man yet?' asked her hostess. 'Not yet, but I'm working on it,' Jane replied smiling. When she and Nigel were on their own after lunch, she told him, 'I know now why I've not seen much of you lately - what a lovely girl you've found.' 'Yes, Geraldine and I get along well together, as long as we keep off the topic of work; but we're just good friends, nothing more,' he said. 'And now, tell me some of your latest escapades, I like hearing about them'. Jane told him the latest about the Spitfire and her chase after the cattle; naturally Nigel asked the pilot's name. 'He's Peter and is in something you'll know all about - PRU.'

'Of course, that explains a lot,' Nigel told her. 'We heard something about some Land girl giving him a rocket, and I did wonder if it was you, then forgot all about it. Poor *chap*! He saved his Spitfire and the country a lot of money by not bailing out, and that's all the thanks he got. Well I'm blowed!'

In the evening, Nigel took the two girls down to the local, where many faces were by now familiar to Jane. They were warmly greeted, and she sat herself down to play dominoes with one elderly acquaintance. Meanwhile, Nigel and Geraldine played darts with another couple, and eventually the evening became quite hilarious. As usual there seemed to be lots of drinking done.

After her partner had well and truly beaten her several times, Jane chatted a while to various people, and then decided to make her way back to the house. Nigel wanted to walk her home but she told him she'd got quite used to walking or cycling in the dark, and besides, he couldn't leave Geraldine on her own.

Land girl Ch 21

The following morning Jane and Nigel, by chance, found themselves walking round his parents' garden together. Jane asked, 'How long are you and Geraldine here for?' 'Only until after lunch today - I just wanted to check up on my folks and it seemed a good moment for them to meet her. We have been good friends for quite some time now, but I'm afraid you've always been uppermost in my heart!'

'Nigel I know what you are saying, but it would never have worked for us. We both knew that! Tom would always have been there. I'm sorry, and hope the two of you will survive this war and find happiness together.' Putting his arm around her shoulders he replied, 'I'm sorry too Jane, but I do understand and hope you will find another Tom before too long. At least we can always be friends - I hope,' and with a nod of agreement she followed him back into the house.

Jane stayed on for a couple more days, during which time she assured her hostess that she had made her peace with Nigel, telling her that they would always remain good friends. Two days later, after giving them their Christmas presents, Jane set off back to the farm. She felt content that a chapter had finally been closed.

Even though it was 10 o'clock by the time she reached home, her family was still at breakfast. She kissed both parents, then her sister and Dusty, and after wishing them a Happy New Year told them she thought she'd go to the village church. Jane seldom found time to attend a church service, and was feeling pleased that today she could manage it, especially on the first day of the New Year. She knew she had much to say thankyou for. She wore her uniform as it was so cold, and after the service many older friends shook her by the hand, and some told her what a grand job she was doing. After she'd had coffee, which was provided after the service at the back of the church, Jane suddenly thought, I must go along to see Michael's mother. This proved to be most fortunate, because she found the poor lady ill in bed, with no one there to look after her. Jane first made her a hot drink, then suggested that she should ask her father to bring his car along to take her to their home until she was back on her feet again. 'I won't take 'no' for an answer,' she said.

Back home, her parents agreed at once and while they fetched Mrs Pick, Jane and her sister started preparing the spare bedroom; they put a hot-water-bottle in the bed, and lit a fire, which immediately gave the room a warm, cosy look designed to cheer up the patient a little. Much later, Mrs Pick drank some of the soup the girls had made for her, and once warm, she soon fell asleep - although her hacking cough could still be heard every now and again. There were many visitors to the house during the afternoon, and sitting by the log-fire later, Jane began to wonder if she'd ever stay awake until the big evening dinner.

This could possibly be Kathleen's last New Year's Day at home, for Dusty was due to sail back to the States in a few months; the GI brides (as their wives were called) were due to follow at a later date. So for all their sakes, she made a big effort - talking to their friends and generally helping her mother, who was also attending to the sick visitor.

'Jane is such a thoughtful girl,' Mrs Pick told Jane's mother. 'She never forgets her old friends, and your having me here is so very much appreciated. I simply have no strength to get anything for myself, and am already feeling better now that I'm not on my own.

As it was quite late by the time the family meal was finished, Jane's dad drove her back to the farm, with her bike tied on the back of his car. She was about to go up to bed when Mrs Freeman telephoned to say she'd forgotten to tell her that a young air-force officer had called that morning hoping to see her, and seemed most disappointed at not finding her there. 'He seemed a very nice young man, and during coffee told me that he'd met you last year, but that it hadn't been a brilliant occasion, for that day he'd most certainly incurred your wrath! I told him that I guessed when that was, which made him laugh!' Jane thanked her for entertaining him, realising it had been Peter, and in a way, wishing she had not missed his visit.

The weather was remarkably good for late February, and after work the next afternoon, she decided to walk Nanna along the road to the blacksmith, whom she knew well as she'd often taken the cart-horses to him for shoeing. Luckily he was still there, and asked Jane what he could do for her. She replied, 'I wonder if you could put some fairly light shoes on my two-year-old here. Can you do it now, or shall I bring her another time?' 'Sure I'll put her some plates on now. Is she quiet about having her feet picked up, and what's her name?' 'It's Nanna, and yes, she is very quiet, just as long as I'm around,' she answered.

'Okay then. You just blow up the fire with them bellows, while I takes a look at her.' Nanna was as good and quiet as Jane had predicted, and after cutting back her hooves a little, the smith soon fitted the shoes on. 'I always love the smell when you put the hot shoe on to the hoof,' Jane told him. 'I believes you've told me that before when you've brought along one of them big 'osses,' he told her with a grin. 'Many thanks for such quick service and now you can get back home to your tea,' the girl told him. Nanna, feeling that something was slightly different, pranced, rather than walked, but Jane anticipating this, held her halter a little tighter and closer to her; it was only a short walk away and soon they were safely back at the stables with the mission accomplished.

The following Saturday was the Land girl's day off, and, catching Dobbin before he went home, she asked if would he give her a hand for a few minutes to hold Nanna. As always, he was pleased to do this, and asked, 'What do you want me to hold her for, Polly?' Jane said, 'I'm going to try putting her saddle on. I think she is ready for more than just being on a leading rein, and as I've already had her bridle on several times, this is the next step.'

First of all, Jane brought Nanna out of her stable with her bridle on, and, talking quietly to her, she slid a cloth across her back, ready for the saddle. No trouble there. Dobbin held her while the girl fetched the new saddle; letting the filly see and sniff it, she slowly eased it across her back over the cloth. Nanna twitched and shivered slightly but that was all. Next came the girth which she put on, quite loosely at first, then slowly tightening it to secure the saddle. She finally added the stirrups. All still calm. 'Carry on gel, don't stop at that,' Dobbin told her, so slowly and carefully Jane put one hand on to the saddle-pommel and with the other on the back of it, pressed down with her full weight. Still no problem, 'Do you think I should get on her or is this enough for one day?' she asked him. 'Get up on her my gal, I'll keep an 'old on 'er 'ead,' he said. Very slowly, Jane eased herself up into the saddle sitting very still. No problem. With her owner patting her neck and at the same time gently touching her sides with her heel, Nanna responded by moving forward slowly, her ears pricking up with anticipation.

After walking her filly around near the stable for a while, they moved out into the lane, where Jane told Dobbin he could let go of the reins. For the first time she and Nanna were on their own, walking as though it had all come naturally. It felt wonderful to Jane; after all this time she was riding her very own mount, which she herself had broken-in. Nanna appeared happy about this weight on her back and moved forward with no trouble at all.

For this first outing they only went as far as the road, Jane not sure if Nanna was up to meeting traffic yet. Unfortunately, the milk-lorry turned into the lane to collect the churns just as they started back. The girl waved the driver down, and he waited until they reached a gateway into a field so that she could turn the horse round to face this great big machine. Only then did Nanna jump about - here was something she'd not seen before, but her rider's soothing voice soon quelled her fears and calmed her down as the lorry drove slowly past. The incident had caused the filly to get into a bit of a lather, but the ever watchful Dobbin was there to lead them back home.

Once back in the stable safe and sound, Jane first of all thanked Dobbin very much for his help, then unsaddled Nanna and rubbed her down before giving her food and water. She went into the farmhouse with a wide grin on her face. 'I've done it!' she told Susan and her boss, 'I've ridden Nanna along the lane and back.' They were so pleased for her, knowing how much time and effort she had put into breaking in her horse for riding. 'Well done! We knew you'd do it sooner or later, and it seems that it's sooner,' said Mrs Freeman.

Later, Jane told Deborah and Susan that she felt like celebrating, 'Let's go out this evening and drink to success.' 'Great! Let's do that,' both girls said at once, 'any excuse for a party.' After supper, just as they were ready, they heard a car peeping its horn outside in the lane. Susan went to see who it was and came back telling Jane that they had got escorts, Peter and Jack. It turned out to be a jolly evening for all: first of all Deborah suggested that they drink a toast to Jane and Nanna, 'And now to Peter,' said Jack, for this very day he'd heard that his friend had been awarded the DFC (Distinguished Flying Cross), which was a very great honour. Looking most embarrassed, Peter, after thanking them, went off to the bar for their drinks while Jack went on to tell them that apparently Peter had taken some very important photographs flying very low along the Rhine some time ago, and the award had just been announced. They all felt pride in his accomplishment and pleased that he had been recognized for it,

After they'd all had quite a few drinks, Jane suggested they went to her home where she was sure her mother would find some food and coffee for them. Her parents, fortunately, were in and very pleased they were to see their daughter, the other two Land girls and the two RAF pilots. After hearing all their news, Jane's father insisted on yet another toast, whilst her mother made sandwiches and coffee. Jane managed a few moments alone with her mother to ask how Mrs Pick was. 'She only went back home a week ago as pleurisy had developed. She really was quite sick for a while,' her mother told her, 'but she now has a friend lodging with her, so at least she's not alone any more.'

'What about Kathleen and Dusty?' was Jane's next question. 'He goes next week, so do try to come and see him, I expect it will be a very tearful parting for your sister,' her mother said, 'and now, by the way, I like your friends; which one is your "special" Jane? I hope though, that you don't get too involved as I see they are both pilots.' 'Okay, Mum. But I do rather like Peter.' Later, on their way back she felt glad that she'd suggested they go to her parents'; her mother had made her see what she had tried to deny to herself, that she really had begun to like Peter quite a lot. Slowly but surely it seemed that the war was coming to a climax. The German Army was retreating on the eastern front, surprised and overwhelmed by the fierceness of the Russian attacks on all sectors of the vast conflict.

In March, Peter told Jane he was falling in love with her; they had been celebrating his birthday in a cosy restaurant when he quietly told her this. His words made her feel pleased and yet strange, even though she'd begun to feel very much the same. Memories of losing Tom still kept returning, although less and less often by now, and yet Peter *was* still on active service. Jane managed to smile at him across the table, telling him in a soft voice, 'I'm really glad, although we'd better not get too serious?' Peter's reply was, '*I'm* serious about *you*, and I don't want to lose you. If the feeling were ever to be mutual I'd be a very happy chap.'

He then told Jane, 'I'm off to Karachi next week to deliver a Spitfire, so be good while I'm away! A couple of my pals have promised they will look after you, and make sure you aren't without company. But be careful, Buck fancies you a bit himself, although he knows full well how I feel!' Jane began to wonder if it was all going to happen again, that she'd fall in love with Peter and then something terrible would happen. She spoke of her fears quite openly to Peter, who was very understanding; he insisted that she must not worry but have faith in him and in the knowledge that he would do his darndest to make sure nothing awful would happen to him. She was a little reassured and vowed to herself that she would not worry.

With those words, they parted, but not before Peter had pressed a piece of paper into Jane's hand and kissed her gently on her lips. Once inside the house, she looked at the paper - it was a poem he'd written just for her. That poem went into the pocket of her dungarees, and every day she took it out and read it - sometimes two or three times - until the paper it was written on was almost like a tissue. Despite her vow not to worry, she was once again aware that she might never see the person she loved again: one of the lines in his poem read 'for I have many weary miles to go', and this haunted her as she thought of all the dangers that lay ahead of him. Later, she thought over and over 'why didn't I tell Peter that I love him too, because I really do'.

Peter was away for five long weeks. Whilst hay-making and rick- thatching left little time for brooding, the weeks went by and there was still no sign of his return; Jane became more and more anxious. Peter's friends tried to keep her cheerful whenever they took her out, although she sensed that even they were getting anxious. Finally, one morning as she was finishing up in the dairy with Deborah, who should walk into the yard but Peter, looking sun-tanned but very tired. On impulse, Jane rushed up to him and throwing herself into his arms, cried, almost in tears *'Am I glad to see you,'* they hugged each other for a moment until she realised how smart he looked and how grubby she was. 'You've been away so long, and I'd imagined all kind of things had happened to you,' Jane told him. Just then Arthur and Dobbin appeared: 'It's good to see you back safe and sound lad, p'raps we'll see a smile on our young Polly's face again now,' one of them said. 'You'd best take the rest of the morning off, lassie,' Arthur told the girl. 'Be back for four o'clock milking though!' Together the two of them walked hand-in-hand across to the farmhouse to let Mrs Freeman know Peter was safely back

'Have some coffee before you go?' she asked them. 'How did you know that I was going anywhere?' Jane asked her boss. 'I know Arthur! I'm sure he's given you some time together.' 'You're quite right - he has,' Peter told her. 'Thank you, a coffee sounds grand.' While they sat around the kitchen table he told his girl why his trip had taken so long. 'I had a tyre burst when I landed at Habaniya to refuel, and would you believe it, they had no spares. So I had to hang around for weeks kicking my heels, until one eventually arrived. Not until then could I complete my trip, and even when I'd done that I had to wait ages for transport back to England. Anyway, here I am! How have you all been, how is Nanna, Jane? I've lots of catching-up to do!'

Later, as the two walked along the lane leading to the road, Peter told Jane he had to be back on the aerodrome by midday, some big-wig was expected and everyone was ordered to be present, but he would be along later in the evening. 'We *are* in the middle of haymaking,' Jane said, 'It could be 9 o'clock before we finish tonight.' 'I'll come along then, our times together are too precious to miss,' he said.

Jane, remembering all her anxious weeks missing him so much said, 'Peter you are right, and I know now just how much I love you. I've waited so long to tell you this and it has been absolute hell for me.' He smiled and hugged her, then pulled something from his jacket pocket, 'I hope you will like this, I noticed you never wear one.' 'This' was a beautiful watch and as he slid it over her hand on to her wrist, Jane exclaimed, 'It's beautiful Peter! Thank you so much - I've never owned one before,' and this time it was Jane who did the kissing!

Soon after his return, Peter was posted to 16 squadron PRU based at Northolt, a squadron that was to provide tactical and strategic reconnaissance for General Montgomery's 21st Army Group in preparation for the invasion of Europe. Once again, she was forced to resign herself to not hearing from him, but like everyone else, she sensed that something BIG was in the air. The U-boat menace in the Atlantic was now much reduced, thanks to the work of intelligence and the enormous scientific and industrial effort put into the creation of effective counter measures. Things were definitely changing.

Hay-making was still in full swing, but the animals were all outside, leaving Jane more time to exercise the horses. Mrs Freeman used Blackie with the trap a good deal for shopping and visiting her friends. All in all things were going well on the farm and Jane was able to ride Nanna often and farther afield. Her young filly was admired by many, not least by Peter, on those rare occasions when he could fly back from Northolt for a short visit. Jane had discovered that he was a keen horseman, and he would occasionally accompany her on the hunter which had belonged to Mr Freeman. The animal had been rather neglected, other than going out on a leading rein when she herself was riding her own horse, so it was wonderful for him to get out.

Harvesting of acres of root crops began almost as soon as the hay was cleared from the fields. The good thing was that Jane could now put Nanna together with Blackie in the same field; it was good for them to have each other's company as there would be little time for riding until this heavy work was done.

The next few weeks were busy for Jane as well as for Peter. But because Jane so rarely heard the news, she was not aware that the D-Day invasion was underway. Then news came that Nigel was missing, not killed, but a prisoner-of-war. Once more her first thoughts were for his parents. She telephoned them that very evening after work. Mrs Gregory was her usual optimistic self, telling Jane that at least he'd now be 'safe for the rest of the war.' It was a strange reaction Jane thought, as there was no knowing how he'd be treated or even where he was. But perhaps this was the only way that a mother could cope with such difficult news. His mother went on to tell her that Nigel's fiancée was taking it very well. It seemed that people had been forced to come to terms with ongoing fear and grief.

Jane had intended to tell Mrs Gregory about Peter but decided that this was *definitely not* the right time. She did say she'd be down to see both she and her husband as soon as the harvesting was finished.

It was Peter who told Jane about Nigel being 'in-the-bag (i.e. a prisoner of war), not knowing about her close relationship with him. Jane then told Peter all about Tom. Some day I'll tell Peter more about Tom's family Jane decided, but not just yet.

The days were dominated by news reports of the allies' progress in all theatres of war, thus the harvest on the farm was accompanied by hard-earned harvests of another kind. Meanwhile, Peter asked Jane if she would like to meet his parents if and when they could arrange some leave together. She said, 'Of course I would! Let's plan to do that before Christmas.' This agreed upon, both set about finding suitable dates for their leave. Mrs Freeman was only too pleased for her Land girl to have time off, and with Susan back from her leave, it was not difficult to arrange once Peter knew when his leave was due.

Land girl Ch 22

Peter and Jane set off on their journey north in the midst of a blizzard. Mrs Freeman insisted on driving them to the station herself, even though visibility was right down to a couple of yards. The progress therefore was slow, interrupted constantly by stopping and clearing the windscreen. When they eventually reached the station, Peter insisted that their driver return right away while she was still able. As she said her goodbyes, Mrs Freeman reminded them to ring her when they'd arrived at their destination, and Peter told her that they would also want to know that she'd got home safely.

Climbing into one of the crowded carriages, they found that most of the occupants were members of the forces, which was not surprising. They too, were in their uniforms with greatcoats on, and it wasn't until Jane removed hers that the occupants realised she was a Land girl, and then right away two army chaps offered them their seats. It was gratifying to know that her work was always so appreciated. Everybody seemed cheerful, despite the discomfort and Jane discovered that most of the sailors, soldiers and airmen were going home on leave. For some, it had been a very long time since they'd seen their loved ones.

The journey north was hazardous in places - parts of the line were covered in snow. However, time did not to matter as there was so much to talk about and so many experiences to share. For Jane and Peter, the fact that they were going to be together for a whole week was reason enough for joy.

On the journey, Peter also put her in the picture about his family, telling her that his father was a police superintendent, and that his mother had been a concert pianist; he had three sisters, all still at school. His only brother was two years older than himself, and was in the army out in Burma. Jane said that she felt a little apprehensive about meeting them all, and Peter quickly assured her that *they* were much looking forward to meeting *her*.

Towards the end of the journey, Jane's eye began to feel tired and heavy: the countryside was covered with snow which reflected and intensified the light as she looked out over the continuous white blanket. Eventually, they reached their station, which, Peter said, was York. Of course, there were no name signs of stations and no announcements because of wartime security. This made everything seem even more uncertain and eerie. They were lucky enough to find a taxi to take them the rest of the way to Peter's home, but even that drive was hazardous because the snow there was on an ice-packed road.

The house was in total blackout; they rang the door-bell and were almost dragged inside. What a welcome they received, absolutely no formality, just love and warmth, happy smiles and lots of chatter! Jane felt at home right away, and sitting by a log-fire with tea and toast she felt she'd known them for a long time.

Much later, when Peter showed her the room upstairs where she was to sleep, he put his arms around her asking, 'Are you all right?' 'Absolutely fine, and already I love your family. But, I hesitate to ask, is your mother alright, she looks so tired and frail?' 'Does she, I hadn't noticed, but then everyone has been milling around her since we arrived. I expect she worries a lot about Laurie, and probably about my flying as well, but I'll have a word with father when she goes to bed. Thanks for pointing it out to me.' 'I just hope we won't be too much extra work for her,' Jane replied, and kissing him goodnight she began to unpack her few things.

In the days that followed, Peter's mother confided in Jane about her fears and her dread at receiving the inevitable 'telegram,' which usually meant a loved one had been killed or captured as a prisoner of war. The mental torment that parents all over the country must be suffering came well and truly home to Jane for she'd not come quite this close to the anguish parents and families were suffering until this moment. From that moment, Jane did all she could to lighten the burden of having two extra mouths to feed; they had both brought their food tokens, and Jane had smuggled a dozen eggs into her suitcase, but it seemed so little when such worry was forever constant, and she so longed to ease the strained look on both parents' faces.

Two days later, she and Peter decided to take a coach trip into the Yorkshire Dales, where Jane had not been before, and even with the snow and icy cold wind the countryside looked lovely in the pale sunshine. By lunchtime they were ravenous, and luckily came across a small inn way up on a hillside; the board outside informed them that the fare they offered was all home-made. Inside, a huge log fire welcomed them; the floors were polished stone flags, the furniture very old and it too, was highly polished. Peter apologised to the landlord about all the snow they'd carried in on their boots. 'Don't worry about that! We're just so delighted to see you, especially in this weather'. He then asked how far they'd come and if they were both hungry'. 'You bet we are!' they said in one voice, and after looking at the menu both decided on soup of the day, to be followed by steak-and-kidney pie with vegetables. The jolly-looking landlord asked if they would care for a glass of his special wine as he would like to drink a toast to them. His wife joined him as he toasted them, their future and their safety. Peter thanking them, wished them 'all the very best' and added, 'We will visit you again once this wretched war is over, and that's a promise.' The meal was excellent and the landlord stayed to chat as they drank coffee; he was interested in Peter's flying as his youngest son had just joined the RAF., and he applauded Jane on doing a 'man's job.'

It was difficult to get away; the warm welcome, the delicious food together with the cosy wood-burning fire made them both feel sleepy. Unfortunately as they saw that the snow was beginning to fall quite fast again they had to bid their kind hosts farewell.

After much slipping and sliding they reached the village and found the coach waiting with its engine running; the driver said, 'We thought you two'd got theeselves lost.' Their journey back was not without problems: once or twice Peter and three other male passengers had to get out and give the coach a push out of a snow-drift.

All the same, both had thoroughly enjoyed the day. At one point on the way back, Jane felt she needed to tell Peter how badly she felt for his mother, and urged him to try to reassure both of his parents as much as he possibly could before they left. The three schoolgirl sisters were back by the time they reached the house and after eyeing Jane up and down, seemed to accept her as their brother's special girl-friend.

One evening, after Jane had bathed and changed into more feminine clothes, Peter dashed up the stairs to her room and, getting down on one knee, asked her to marry him. This took her completely and utterly by surprise; she was sure Peter had understood her when she'd said, only a short while ago, that they must not get too serious until the war was over - or at least until his tour of operations was finished.

'Peter, let's not tempt fate, I daren't give you an answer now. Maybe we could be engaged until peace is declared.' Although he looked a little downhearted, he took her answer very well. 'Okay, let's be engaged. You have made me so happy - I want to tell Mum and Dad now, if that's all right by you?'

They told his parents their news; both were pleased and gave them their blessing, while the younger ones nudged each other and giggled, as sisters do. Later on, Jane rang to tell her parents. Although they too were happy for them, there was a slight hesitation and then, 'Of course we're pleased. But we're also pleased that it's only an engagement until the war is over.'

Altogether it was a very happy visit, and Jane was pleased to know that Peter had had a long discussion first of all with his father and then with both parents together. His father promised that he'd see that his wife had a thorough check-up with her doctor, and would let him know the outcome. They left the family on yet another cold, frosty morning, but Jane felt that she knew them all now and they would no longer be strangers in her mind, but a loving and happy family.

Returning to her farm work once more, Jane felt happier knowing that she really did belong to someone again. Unlike Tom, Peter hadn't mentioned anything about an engagement-ring, 'Perhaps he thinks it's unwise for you to wear a ring doing the kind of jobs we do on the farm,' suggested Deborah, when Jane confided in her.

As that most tempestuous year, 1944, drew to its close, the allied air offensive maintained its powerful and devastating onslaught on the industrial areas and cities of Germany. The daylight raids by bombers of the Eighth US Air Force, combined with night bombing by the Royal Air Force's Bomber Command, resulted in a 'round-the-clock' assault on the third Reich. At long last final victory seemed not quite so far away.

Nevertheless, many of the air-crews known to Peter, Susan and Jane had been lost; these were still very anxious days. Many pilots, who had given their all, were becoming tired and needed a rest from operations, but sadly, young air-crews fresh from training and with little experience were more vulnerable to enemy flak and fighters. Peter had a few operations remaining, but still each one became a nightmare to Jane. She wondered constantly if his luck would run out. She was not at all her usual relaxed self, and even Nanna sensed this when Jane was riding her; consequently, she began to play up and occasionally even threw her rider off.

Mrs Freeman suggested Jane might allow Geoff to give Nanna a good gallop now and then, to show the young filly just who *was* the boss. With a heavy heart, the girl agreed to this, knowing that she was, right now, not in total control. She knew that Geoff had very light hands, and also a soft voice with horses. She reluctantly conceded to her boss's suggestion which turned out to be a good one.

As the farming year came to a close once more, any spare time the men had was spent on preparing machinery for the coming hay, corn and root harvests. Jane again began to throw herself into her own job, and tried to worry less about her fiancé.

One morning, to her great surprise, Jane received a very happy letter from Pat. The surprise was all the greater as she'd not been the best correspondent, and her letters had been few and far between. This one though was full of happy news: she and Bob were to be married in October and she wanted Jane to be her bridesmaid. Pat also said she hoped as many as possible from the farm would be able to attend. That evening, Jane rang Pat to say how pleased she was to be asked and that she would love to be her bridesmaid.

When her next two days-off arrived, having received instructions from Pat as to her whereabouts on a farm near Cranwell in Lincolnshire, Jane was very excited at the prospect of seeing her very good friend again. Mrs Freeman drove her to the station, where she caught her first train on the journey; this was followed by two other trains before she eventually got through to Sleaford. Pat had said that she and Bob would meet her there, and it was an excited couple of Land girls who hugged one another joyfully as they met again after three long years. Bob did manage to greet Jane but could hardly get a word in as the girls had a lot to tell one another; he just steered them over to his battered old car and seating them in the back, proceeded to drive towards Cranwell. Naturally their talk soon turned to the wedding and clothes and as they reached the farmhouse where Pat lived, Bob told them that he'd pick them up later for dinner.

Jane thought right away what a tidy and well-kept farm Pat was on. She immediately took to the farmer and his wife, and could see that they had the same kind of relationship with their Land girl as she had with her boss. As Pat had no parents, the farmer, Mr Chamberlain, had agreed to give her away, and their two small daughters were to be bridesmaids with Jane. Things seemed to be getting pretty well organised for Pat's big day.

Eventually the two girls were able to talk about their hopes for the future, and Pat who had known about Tom being killed, said how pleased she was that her friend had found someone else. Inwardly, she voiced a little alarm that he was also a pilot at present on operational duties. Later, after Jane had told her of her faith in his coming safely through, Pat was full of admiration for her friend's optimism.

The evening with Bob proved to Jane that he really was the right person for Pat; his feet were firmly on the ground, and he had already set his thoughts to the kind of job he hoped for once the war was over. He had a married quarter in his sights for after the wedding, and seemed in total control of their future together. More than that, he absolutely adored Pat, and vice-versa. They had a wartime dinner together and Jane caught up on all their news. Before she left, Bob told Jane that although Pat loved her farm life in Lincolnshire, she would still prefer to be back in Oxfordshire; he said he would try to get posted back in the following year, and hopefully they could settle there.

Having made all the plans to return to the farm on the evening before the wedding, Pat and Jane caught a bus to the railway station. Hugs and farewells exchanged, Jane got into an almost empty carriage for the first part of her journey back; once more there were two more changes and at each one men in all kinds of uniforms bundled in. The carriages yet again soon filled with cigarette smoke, together with lots of chatter and the occasional song. Jane felt very proud to be British - these young chaps would never let their country down she felt sure, yet they were all so *very young.*

There was a letter from Peter when she got to the farmhouse; he told her he was off to Brussels with his squadron, with now only five more operations to do, and then hopefully some leave. *Then would she consider marrying him?* Jane had to think long and hard about this. She had said 'not while he was still on operations' and now he was only five away from finishing. It would be tempting fate, five more were five more and still his luck might not last. Should she think like this? If she loved him enough should she write and say yes? It was a dilemma only she could solve.

Yet again fate stepped in. She was out riding Nanna with Mrs Freeman on her horse, and as they rode along she talked her problem over with her. Because of what had happened to her own husband and because of Tom getting killed her boss advised Jane to talk it over with her own parents and then make her decision. As an afterthought, she reminded Jane, 'You are still only 23 years old.'

When they reached the farm, Jane was about to put the two horses away as Susan rushed out. Seeing her white face and tearful eyes they both asked what was wrong? Susan told Jane it was news about Peter. 'He has been shot down and taken a pr...prisoner of w...war. Oh, I'm so sorry to be the one telling you this, but the m...message just came through from the aerodrome and someone from there is on his way to see you.' Jane took a gulp of air and then vented:'This blasted, bloody war, will it never end, will we never have peace of mind again? I can't believe this has happened, but I suppose in my heart I knew it might.'

Mrs Freeman, herself almost in tears for her Land girl, said, 'I'll see to the horses, Jane. You go on inside.' 'No, I will do my job with them, and the calves still have to be fed. Things just have to go on, that much I *have* learned. Thank you Susan, I'm only sorry it had to be you taking the message. Don't worry, I will cope. Let's get on with our work.' Abruptly, she turned away.

Both Mrs Freeman and Susan were amazed to watch Jane as she silently finished dealing with the two horses, feeding and bedding them down, before going over to see to her calves. Was there no end to what she could cope with! The news soon reached the other men who were equally embarrassed as to what to say to their Polly.

Later that evening her friend Mike appeared; he had been asked to see Jane and give her the facts that they had so far. It seemed Peter was on a low-level sortie with 16 squadron, 34 Wing, 2nd Tactical Air Force photographing fortifications along the Rhine from Nijmegen to Emmerich when flak hit his aircraft. He was forced to bail out. He had managed to hide for a while but sadly was picked up by a German patrol. As far as they knew, he would be a prisoner of war, but they knew not where. Mike watched the girl trying bravely not to break down, but as his arm went around her she could no longer hold back her tears and cries of grief; he quietly said under his breath, 'Bugger and blast this war.'

Life on the farm carried on much as in previous autumns; Jane had had no choice but to come to terms with Peter being a wartime prisoner, and became almost her old cheerful self once more. Nanna certainly knew who was in charge when she was led out of the field, bridled and saddled with Jane on her back again. No more nonsense from her now, and only when her owner had time off for her friend's wedding in October did she have Geoff riding her. He, in fact, started to teach Nanna to jump obstacles, and found her a natural at it. Geoff couldn't wait for Jane's return to show her what Nanna could do, but her return was delayed for a week as the Land girl went down to see Tom's parents before returning to the farm. She especially wanted to tell them all about Peter, how they came to meet, and how their romance had progressed; she had written to tell them she had found someone, and they in return had said how pleased they were for her. Now she felt it time to tell them of hers and Peter's engagement and that he, like their son, was a prisoner of war.

On the journey to Poole, Jane thought again and again of the happy wedding she had been to - she was overjoyed for her friends Pat and Bob. It had all been quite perfect: Pat, a beautiful bride with a handsome groom, two lovely little bridesmaids in their velvet dresses, and she herself feeling extremely feminine in a matching long velvet gown. She had had a moment of feeling self-pity, wishing it was Peter and herself, but seeing her friends so very happy and so much in love, she could only join in and be happy with them.

One day ..... it would happen one day, the war had to end, it simply had to. Meantime, she must have faith, and continue to pray for Peter and for the thousands and thousands of other young men who were still fighting for their country.